LEAN

POCKET GUIDE

CONTROL · DEFINE · MEASURE · ANALYZE · IMPROVE

LEAN

RATH & STRONG
Management Consultants
Founded in 1935

ISBN 0-9746328-9-9

Second Printing, May 2007

Rath & Strong Management Consultants
45 Hayden Avenue
Suite 2700
Lexington, Massachusetts 02421
Tel: 781/861-1700
e-mail: info@rathstrong.com
www.rathstrong.com

BY
Charlene Adair

DESIGN/PRODUCTION
Jean F. Drew, *graphic and cover design*
Rodd Welch, *project manager*

Foreword

Rath & Strong's Lean Pocket Guide captures the essence of Lean in a useful and easy-to-follow format. This practical, hands-on guide could only have been created by a firm that is grounded in history and experience while being led by innovators of the future.

Lean is part of our heritage. Rath & Strong pioneered Lean by helping bring this powerful concept to the West in the 1970s, as we created work cells modeled after the Toyota Production System and became the world leaders of Just-In-Time.

Rath & Strong has been in the business of providing fundamental principles and tools for process improvement since 1935. Through our vast hands-on experience, we have learned what *really* works in any company or business process — service, administrative, or manufacturing — to achieve lasting, measurable results.

Our ground-breaking approach to Lean using the DMAIC problem-solving methodology makes it easy to integrate Lean and Six Sigma, and the step-by-step approach in this guide makes it an integral part of your improvement efforts.

Special thanks to Charlene Adair for her work on this publication. Rath & Strong is delighted to bring our practical knowledge of Lean to you in this Pocket Guide! We are excited to have it join our list of *Wall Street Journal* best-selling business books.

Daniel L. Quinn
President and CEO

Aon Management Consulting/Rath & Strong

INTRODUCTION: What is Lean? 1
Integrating Lean into the DMAIC Methodology

DEFINE: 9

   Chapter 1. *Identifying a Product Family* 9
   to Determine the Project Scope

MEASURE: 15

   Chapter 2. *Mapping the Current State* 15
   Value Stream to Identify Waste

   Chapter 3. *Mapping a Process to* 27
   Understand and Improve

ANALYZE: 33

   Chapter 4. *Creating a Lean Future State* 33
   Value Stream Map

   Chapter 5. *Selecting the Right Project to Begin* 49
   Making the Lean Value Stream a Reality

   Chapter 6. *Analyzing Time and Work* 55

   Chapter 7. *Analyzing Equipment Effectiveness* 61

   Chapter 8. *Analyzing Equipment through* 67
   Total Productive Maintenance

   Chapter 9. *Analyzing Equipment Setup* 75

IMPROVE: 83

   Chapter 10. *Creating a Cell Layout* 83
   for Ultimate Flow

   Chapter 11. *Staffing a Cell to Meet Takt Time* 95

Chapter 12. *Standardizing for Flexibility* 107

Chapter 13. *Maintaining Order through 5S and* 115
    Visual Workplace

Chapter 14. *Improving Ergonomics* 129
    for Health and Safety

Chapter 15. *Mistake-Proofing the Improvements* 135

Chapter 16. *Using Kaizen Workshops* 141
    for Quick Focused Improvements

Chapter 17. *Planning, Implementing, and* 149
    Debugging Improvements

CONTROL: 157

    Chapter 18. *Making Changes a Way of Life* 157

Index 161

WHAT IS LEAN?

INTEGRATING LEAN INTO THE DMAIC METHODOLOGY

Lean **eliminates waste** and creates **continuous flow** in any Value Stream. A **Value Stream** is all of the actions, both value-creating and non value-creating, required to bring a product from order to delivery. This includes actions to process information and transform the product. Lean creates a foundation for continuous improvement within the Value Stream.

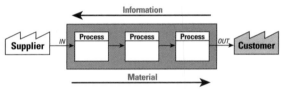

Even though the roots of Lean stem from the Toyota Production System as a a set of manufacturing principles and tools, it has evolved through the years under terms such as Just-in-Time and Process Redesign and has proven to be just as effective in transactional, office, and service environments as it is in manufacturing. Therefore, the product may be a widget that is being manufactured, a service that is being provided, or a transaction completed successfully.

Lean is:

- A way to understand value from the viewpoint of the customer and eliminate waste — activities that don't add value
- A methodology to increase velocity and create a continuous flow of value-adding activities, pulled by the customer
- A set of tools to continuously improve this flow

Lean is NOT:
- Less space
- Fewer people
- Limited resources
- Efficiency no matter what
- Not enough supplies
- Giving the customer the bare minimum

HOW LEAN WORKS WITH SIX SIGMA

Lean and Six Sigma are complimentary, since Six Sigma eliminates variation and defects, both of which can create havoc when trying to eliminate waste and create continuous flow. And, of course, the opposite can occur as well: having waste and lack of continuous flow can cause us to eliminate variation and defects in a process that doesn't even add value!

Lean has been organized within the DMAIC problem-solving methodology so that it can easily be integrated into an existing Six Sigma effort, or to add Six Sigma to your Lean effort later.

WHAT IS WASTE?

Elimination of **waste** requires us to define value as:
- The activity physically changes the work product (or adds important information)
- The activity must not be "rework"
- The customer must be willing to pay for it

Non value-added activities can be categorized as pure waste or **Business Value**. Business Value includes activities required by the business, but not by the customer, such as legal or tax filing.

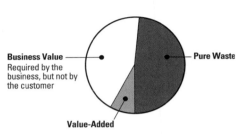

Business Value — Required by the business, but not by the customer

Pure Waste

Value-Added

The traditional seven wastes are:

- Defects
- Overproduction
- Waiting
- Transport
- Extra processing
- Inventory
- Motion

In addition, the office environment has:

- Handoffs between people and departments
- Scatter, or continually rescheduling and reprioritizing
- Useless information for status or reporting
- Discarded knowledge — not making it available to others
- Wrong tools
- Barriers to communication

WHAT IS CONTINUOUS FLOW?

Continuous flow results when the product (can be a widget, service, or transaction) is produced and moved from one processing step to the next, one-at-a-time, without stoppages, scrap, or backflow. We look for consistent flow rates that are regular, linear, and have even capacity utilization — synchronized with the customer.

Think of the conductor of an orchestra as the customer and the orchestra as the activities within a value stream. The drumbeat keeps the value stream in sync with the customer.

With no drumbeat, we experience peaks and valleys in workload (hurry up and wait), and the rate of production is set by the capabilities of machines or people.

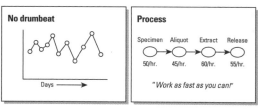

With a drumbeat, we have a level work load with a common rate that applies to the entire Value Stream.

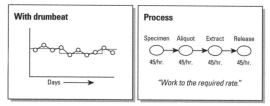

Takt time is the measure to indicate how often we need to complete a product (or how often the drum should beat) to be synchronized with customer demand.

$$\text{Takt Time} = \frac{\text{Available Time per Day}}{\text{Customer Demand per Day}}$$

Available time per day is the time that the process can run if there is product to work on.

Pull is a system in which work is done only in response to a signal from the customer or from a downstream process that indicates a need for more product.

WHAT IS CONTINUOUS IMPROVEMENT?

Lean seeks perfection through continuous improvement:
- There is no end to the process of reducing effort, time, space, cost, and defects while offering the customer a product they actually want
- When value flows faster, more waste is exposed in the Value Stream
- The more the product is pulled, the more impediments to flow are revealed so they can be removed

In Summary, Lean Is Often Counterintuitive!
- Slow down in order to speed up
- Stop activity so work never stops
- Perfection is the aim, never the claim
- "Standards" should always change
- Local efficiency does not equal global efficiency

INTEGRATING LEAN INTO THE DMAIC METHODOLOGY

DMAIC is a universal problem-solving methodology that has been followed by Six Sigma for a number of years.

The Lean objectives for each phase of DMAIC are:

DEFINE: Select and begin defining the project Value Stream.

MEASURE: Complete a Current State Value Stream Map to establish a process baseline for the Value Stream.

ANALYZE: Analyze the Value Stream to design a Value Stream with the shortest lead time, the highest quality, and the lowest cost possible.

IMPROVE: Design, implement, and debug a continuous flow cell with the shortest lead time, the highest quality, and the lowest cost possible.

CONTROL: Ensure that the new Value Stream meets/exceeds goals and that the new design can be further improved.

The following graphic shows how the steps in Lean integrate into the DMAIC methodology. You will see how Lean follows the same methodology, making Lean Six Sigma a natural progression in your quest to improve Value Streams.

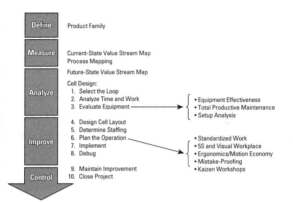

HOW TO USE THIS POCKET GUIDE

Chapters listed in the Table of Contents follow the steps listed above to implement Lean in any Value Stream. The Index sends you directly to specific terms and formulas.

Good luck as you apply the power of Lean to your business process!

IDENTIFYING A PRODUCT FAMILY
TO DETERMINE THE PROJECT SCOPE

DETERMINING THE PROJECT SCOPE

Determining the project scope is a bit like peeling the onion —
one layer at a time. We can use a high-level SIPOC, which identi-
fies the **S**upplier, **I**nputs, **P**rocesses, **O**utputs, and **C**ustomers, or a
strategic Value Stream Map for the entire company, to "peel
the onion" down to a manageable level.

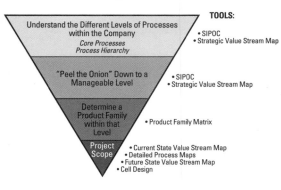

TOOLS:

Understand the Different Levels of Processes within the Company
Core Processes
Process Hierarchy
- SIPOC
- Strategic Value Stream Map

"Peel the Onion" Down to a Manageable Level
- SIPOC
- Strategic Value Stream Map

Determine a Product Family within that Level
- Product Family Matrix

Project Scope
- Current State Value Stream Map
- Detailed Process Maps
- Future State Value Stream Map
- Cell Design

Then, we identify Product Families within that level to determine a
manageable scope for an improvement project.

WHAT IS A PRODUCT FAMILY?

A **Product Family** is a group of products that use the same or
similar processing steps and equipment within the selected Value
Stream, or scope. Product Families are the most effective unit for
analyzing a Value Stream.

WHY IDENTIFY PRODUCT FAMILIES?
We identify Product Families to better define a Value Stream project scope, to identify specific inputs and outputs, and to get greater detail when we begin mapping the Value Stream. This allows us to set more specific improvement goals and focus on a manageable process improvement project. After all, if a Value Stream represents the flow of the product, the Value Stream Map (VSM) cannot map more than one product flow with any clarity.

USING A PRODUCT FAMILY MATRIX TO IDENTIFY PRODUCT FAMILIES

Steps to identify Product Families using a **Product Family Matrix** include:

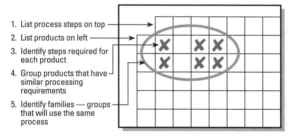

1. List process steps on top
2. List products on left
3. Identify steps required for each product
4. Group products that have similar processing requirements
5. Identify families — groups that will use the same process

Process steps need to be listed in enough detail to show differences in processes, but not at the work step level. Products do not have to have exactly the same process steps to be in the same family, but they should have roughly 80 percent of the same processing steps. Additional data may be required to determine if differences are significant or not.

Products should be listed in enough detail to show differences in the processes each passes through. Products are fairly easy to identify in a manufacturing company — they are usually what the company makes and sells. It is more challenging to determine what the products are in a service or transactional Value Stream. You can easily fall into traps in defining the product!

Type of Value Stream	Product Family	Product Trap
Manufacturing	One model of laptop computers	Product clear because built piece by piece
Service	A related series of blood tests	We could follow the test tube, but it is the information that is being sold
Transactional	Completed staffing request for VPs	We might do this by department, but it is the level within the organization that determines the process required

The following is an example of a completed Product Family:

1. Identify Product and Process Steps

2. Rearrange
3. Find Families

Process Steps and Equipment							
	1	2	3	4	5	6	7
A	X			X	X		
B	X	X			X		X
C	X			X	X		
D	X	X	X			X		X
E							

Process Steps and Equipment							
	1	2	3	4	5	6	7
A	X			X	X		
C	X			X	X		
B	X	X		X		X	
D	X	X	X			X		X
E							

VALIDATING PRODUCT FAMILIES

A **Spaghetti Diagram** can be used in most Value Streams to validate product families. A Spaghetti Diagram shows the actual path taken by a product as it travels through the processes of the Value Stream.

By differentiating each product on a physical layout (or transactions through different systems and departments), it is easy to verify which products travel through primarily the same process path. This is also a good test for the level of detail chosen to determine Product Families.

The following chart is an example of a Spaghetti Diagram of two products — one represented by the dotted line and the other by the solid line. Given the very different paths through the processes, this confirms two product families.

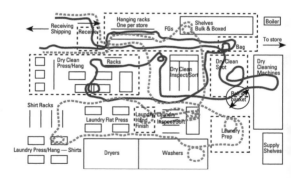

©2006 Rath & Strong/Aon Management Consulting

SELECTING A PRODUCT FAMILY

In order to decide what to work on first, identified Product Families need to be prioritized based on criteria such as:

- Disparity with customer expectations
- Importance to company strategy
- Opportunity for improvement
- Ease or speed of implementation

CONCLUSION

Once a Product Family is selected, then it is time to move on to the Measure Phase of DMAIC and Value Stream Mapping.

MAPPING THE CURRENT STATE VALUE STREAM TO IDENTIFY WASTE

WHY USE A VALUE STREAM MAP?

A Value Stream is all of the actions, both value-creating and non value-creating, required to bring a product from order to delivery, so a **Value Stream Map** (VSM) is a "picture" of the Value Stream from the product's point of view. *This is not a flow chart of what people do, but what happens to the product (a widget, service, electronic record, etc.) as it flows through the Value Stream*. A Value Stream Map helps us:

- See the entire Value Stream in one picture using a common language
- Work on and improve the bigger picture versus individual processes
- Include information and material flows in addition to the product flow creating a "3-D" picture of the Value Stream
- Identify waste and see the flow, tying together Lean concepts and techniques

THE LANGUAGE OF VALUE STREAM MAPPING

Consistent icons are needed to create a clear picture of the Value Stream:

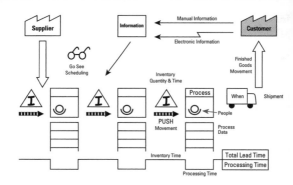

STEPS TO CREATE A CURRENT STATE VALUE STREAM MAP

GUIDELINES FOR DRAWING THE CURRENT STATE
VALUE STREAM MAP

- At least one person (preferable the entire team) should walk the entire Value Stream
- Use pencil and paper or post-it notes and draw by hand to maintain ultimate flexibility
- Use the standard language (icons)
- Get real data — don't depend on process documentation
- Erase and modify as you learn more
- Follow the smallest unit of the product possible — the Value Stream Map maps "one unit" as you have defined it

You may want to begin with a quick walk through the Value Stream and then go back for details beginning with the customer to ensure that all branches of the Value Stream are captured. Be sure to adhere to all process area etiquette by following normal protocol for visitors and not disrupting the workflow. *Be open about the fact that you are evaluating the work process, not the people*!

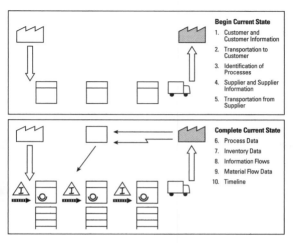

The challenge in collecting data for the Current State Value Stream Map is to collect enough data to baseline the Value Stream and identiy opportunities to improve time and flow, but to not collect so much data that you are buried in it for long periods of time.

Steps 1 and 2: Customer and Customer Information,
Transportation to Customer

Include:

- A clear specification of value
- Requirements with all relevant detail including quantities, mix, batch/package size, working hrs., trends, seasonality, etc.
- Delivery frequency and mode if important
- Any other relevant data

Step 3: Identification of Processes

Include:

- Process boxes that indicate where material is flowing without significant inventory wait time
- A picture of the flow left to right including parallel processes and branches

Step 4 and 5: Supplier and Supplier Information, Transportation from the Supplier

Include:

- The flow for 1 or 2 main suppliers
- Batch/package size and delivery frequency
- Any other relevant data

Below is a Current State Value Stream Map completed through step 5. This Value Stream could be producing anything: a widget (receive parts, assemble the parts, pack and ship the widget), a service (receive laundry, wash and press the laundry, bag or box laundry and deliver), or a transaction (receive information, input information electronically and make calculations, format conclusions and summary and e-mail to customer).

Step 6: Process Data

A Data Collection Plan will be needed as we add the data boxes to each process step. Each data box should include all relevant information about that process. Key data items for consideration are described below. However, data items should not be limited to those below, but should include anything that better describes each process.

Time measurement is extremely important in Lean, since it is a key indicator of waste and flow. **Value added time** (VA) is the time needed to complete only those work elements (or steps within each process) that are value-added. Of course, an entire process could be deemed non-value added!

Lead time (LT) is the elapsed time it takes a product (one piece/unit as defined in the Value Stream Map) to move through the defined Value Stream start to finish.

Processing time (PT) is the elapsed time from the time the product enters a process until it leaves that process. In the example Value Stream, the processes are receive, assemble, and pack and ship. Processing time can be considered the lead time for a particular process.

Cycle time (CT) is how often a product is completed by a process. This is a RATE measure, not an elapsed time measure. We can measure the cycle time at any point in the Value Stream by determining at that particular point the rate at which product is being produced. Cycle time can be calculated for a process by dividing the processing time by the number of people or machines doing the work.

Setup time (SU) is the elapsed time from the last good product unit of the prior batch until normal production rate is reached on the new batch. Setup time includes activities such as loading, unloading, testing, trial runs, etc.

Uptime (UT) is the percent of time the process actually operates compared to the planned operating time for the process assuming product is available. This measure is typically associated with machine variability.

Capacity is the maximum output for a process, and **batch size** is the quantity of product worked on and moved at one time.

Pack size, or **pack-out quantity**, is the quantity of product required by the customer for movement or shipment. **Product variation**, or **mix**, refers to the number of different product types or models being processed.

Rework Rate is the percent of total product that does not meet the customer's requirement and must be worked on again. This usually requires looping back in the process or a special process.

Scrap Rate is the percent of total product that does not meet the customer's requirement and must be discarded for zero or salvage value.

Defect Rate is the percent of total product that does not meet the customer's requirement and includes both rework and scrap.

Number of people in each process is calculated using a "full time equivalent" calculation. For example, if one person works half time in a process, then the number of people = .5.

Available time per day is the time that the Value Stream can run if there is product to work on. Therefore, if all people in the process take their breaks and/or lunch together, then that time is deducted from the available time. On the other hand, if people stagger their breaks and/or lunch, the Value Stream can run continuously and that time is not deducted.

Typically, setup time and unplanned downtime are not deducted because we want to keep the spotlight on reducing these times. Planned downtime is usually deducted since it is a preventative activity that is designed to keep the process running. However, if it is clear that waste can be eliminated from planned downtime activities, we may decide to not deduct planned downtime from available time.

The example below shows the relevant process data for this Value Stream. Note that cycle time was calculated using the processing time and the number of people in each process. The cycle time for this entire Value Stream is 4m — we assume that the prior processes do something to keep up (probably overtime).

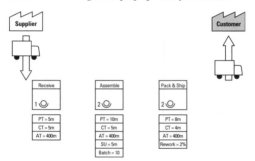

Step 7: Inventory data

Inventory data is very important because if a product is in inventory, it is waiting. Waiting is waste and causes lead times to be longer. Lots of waiting in any process indicates poor product flow. Several categories of inventory are described below.

Raw material (RM) is material, or work, that has not yet been processed by the Value Stream as defined. **Work-in-process** (WIP) is product being processed and **finished goods** (FG) is product that is completed by the Value Stream but awaiting shipment to the customer.

Buffer stock is product held at the downstream end of the Value Stream to protect the customer from starvation if the process cannot produce as needed. **Safety stock** is product held at any point within the Value Stream to prevent downstream processes from starvation if the process cannot produce as needed. **Shipping stock** is product at the downstream end of the Value Stream that is building up for the next shipment.

Inventory turns is a measure of how quickly materials are moving through the Value Stream. It is calculated by dividing the total cost of goods by the average inventory on hand.

Step 8: Information Flows
Information flow tells each process what to make or do next. Examples of information flow are schedules, priorities, forecasts, etc. The question to ask is: *"How can we flow information so that one process will make only what the next process needs when it needs it?"*

Step 9: Material Flow Data
Movement of the product (or material/information to make the product) is a focus of Lean improvement. Material is typically "pushed" through most Value Streams; Lean helps us create processes whereby the customer "pulls" material through the Value Stream as needed.

Step 10: Timeline
As we have said, lead time is a key indicator of waste and flow in any Value Stream. The timeline in the Value Stream Map tells us

how long it take one unit (as defined earlier) to move through the entire Value Stream. Steps to develop the timeline include:

1. Determine the available time — this becomes the baseline time for "a day".

2. Determine the average (or median) production rate per day. This is the "middle" volume that you are basing the Value Stream map on. Variations in that volume will be accounted for later.

3. Determine the processing time for each process in the Value Stream.

4. Determine the time that one unit waits in inventory on average in each inventory location. We use **Little's Law** to translate inventory into lead time:

> *Inventory = Production Rate x Lead Time*
> or
> *Lead Time = Inventory ÷ Production Rate*

COMPLETED CURRENT STATE VALUE STREAM MAP (VSM)

The Value Stream Map below illustrates the addition of inventory data, information flows, material flow data, and the timeline. *Note that setup time was allocated per unit, or piece, and added to the processing time to create a realistic timeline*. Little's Law was used to convert the average inventory in units to lead time. This Value Stream builds 100 units per day using the 400 minutes per day of available time as the baseline.

	Receive	Assemble	Pack & Ship
	1	2	2
PT	PT = 5m	PT = 10m	PT = 8m
CT	CT = 5m	CT = 5m	CT = 4m
AT	AT = 400m	AT = 400m	AT = 400m
		SU = 5m	Rework = 2%
		Batch = 10	

50 units   25 units   10 units   100 units

200 m   100 m   40 m   400 m | Total LT = 763.5 m |
5 m   10.5 m   8 m | Total PT = 23.5 m |

Note that in this example, we allocated the setup time per piece and included it in the timeline calculation. Another option is to assume that the setup time is accounted for in the extra wait time caused by having to accumulate and process a batch of 10 at a time. The important issue is that you have an accurate measure of how long it takes for one unit to move through the Value Stream and that we highlight waste, such a long setups.

VALUE STREAM MAPPING COMPLEX FLOWS

Most Value Streams aren't as simple as the one above. Parallel processes are very common such as the one shown below.

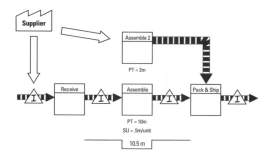

In this case, Assemble2 runs parallel with Assemble, and all the product/information comes together at Pack & Ship. The rule of thumb is to use the longer of the two processing times for the timeline.

In other cases, the product may split at some point in the Value Stream, such as below.

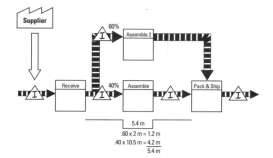

60 percent is processed by Assemble2 and 40 percent is processed by Assemble. You can see that we simply weighted the processing times to develop the timeline entry.

CONCLUSION
The Current State Value Stream Map is now complete. We have a "3-D" picture of what happens in this Value Stream and many opportunities for improvement become obvious.

MAPPING A PROCESS TO UNDERSTAND AND IMPROVE

In some cases, we need to understand more about a particular process within the Value Stream before or during Future State design. **Process Mapping** can be used for this purpose in Measure and Analyze to determine detailed steps in a process.

Use Process Mapping sparingly as a way to apply a magnifying glass to a process. For instance, if the example Value Stream is a service such as a laundry and you need to know more about Assemble, we might expand this process into steps. *Process Mapping should* NEVER *be used **instead of** Value Stream Mapping in Lean*!

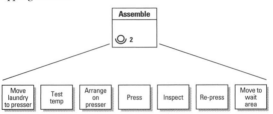

WHY USE PROCESS MAPPING

Process mapping...

- Creates a common understanding
- Clarifies the steps in a process
- Uncovers problems in the process
- Reveals how the process operates
- Helps identify improvement opportunities in a process (complexity, waste, delays, inefficiencies and bottlenecks)

The focus in Measure is to understand the process in order to improve it later.

ACTIVITY AND DEPLOYMENT PROCESS MAPS

Activity process maps are specific about what happens in the process step by step. Again, Lean insists that we map what happens to the product (widget, service, or transaction), not what people do!

Deployment process maps show the steps in the process along with what people or groups are involved in each step.

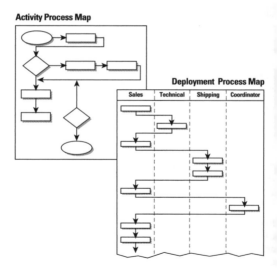

Activity Process Map

Deployment Process Map

Sales	Technical	Shipping	Coordinator

VALUE ADDED ANALYSIS MAPPING

Value added analysis mapping is used to identify:

- Non-value added steps
- Lead time
- Any other waste, including other process problems

VALUE ADDED FLOW ANALYSIS

The purpose of a **value added flow analysis** (VAFA) is to determine which steps add value and to determine the percentage of steps and time these value added steps represent. An example of a value added flow analysis for the assemble process is shown below.

Step	Time — minutes	VA
Move laundry	5	
Test temp	2	
Arrange on presser	2	
Press	2	2
Inspect	3	
Re-press	1	
Move to wait area	5	
Totals	20	2

In the assemble process above, press is the only value added step in the entire process, representing only 14 percent of the steps and 10 percent of the time. In a typical process, *less than 17 percent of all steps and 5 percent of all lead time is value added!*

VALUE ANALYSIS MATRIX

Specific types of non-value added time can be tracked with a **value analysis matrix**. This helps clarify not only the types of waste present in the process, but also the percentage of the overall process each non-value added step adds. In the process below, it is clear that we would want to work on movement and possibly defects first.

Process Step	1	2	3	4	5	6	7	8	9	10	Total	% Total
Time (hours)	12	10	1	10	20	6	10	1	10	20	100	100%
Value-Added			*					*			2	2%
Non Value-Added												
Inventory (WIP, Backlog)									*		10	10%
Delay (Operator)												
Duplication						*					6	6%
Movement		*			*					*	52	52%
Defects (Customer)		*		*			*				30	30%
Rework (Internal)												
Checking												
Lost Opportunities												
Total											100	100%

TIME-BASED VALUE ADDED FLOW ANALYSIS

The following **time-based value added flow analysis** shows the amount of value added time compared to the total lead time by process and for the overall Value Stream.

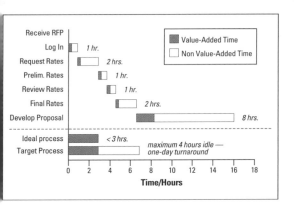

CONCLUSION

Lean brings value analysis to process mapping, forming a powerful tool used to understand and improve any process.

CREATING A LEAN FUTURE STATE VALUE STREAM MAP

A Lean Value Stream consists of value-adding activities that produce a product

- Exactly as the customer needs it
- When the customer needs it
- In the least amount of lead time (best flow)
- At the pace the customer needs it

A Lean Value Stream has the shortest lead time, the highest quality, and the lowest cost possible.

Lean offers a set of concepts and tools that help us build a future state Lean Value Stream one step at a time.

CREATING A FUTURE STATE VALUE STREAM MAP

Steps to create a **Future State Value Stream Map** include:

1. Begin by drawing on the Current State Value Stream map and adding to the data collection plan as you go.

2. Develop the Lean design and draw the new Value Stream map by answering eight questions (see next section) in sequence.

3. Create a realistic, doable plan by doing what you can with what you have. In other words, don't plan in a futuristic capability that hasn't been invented yet!

Below are new icons to add to the value stream mapping "language" for Future State Value Stream Mapping.

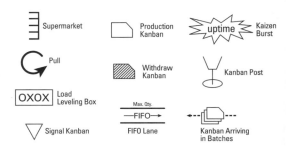

EIGHT QUESTIONS TO BUILD A LEAN VALUE STREAM

The following eight questions should be answered in sequence. Each question will be discussed in this chapter.

1. What is the Takt time?

2. Build directly to shipping or to a finished goods supermarket?

3. Where can continuous flow be used?

4. Where are pull systems needed?

5. At what single point (the pacemaker) in the Value Stream is production triggered?

6. How is production mix leveled at the pacemaker?

7. How is production volume leveled at the pacemaker?

8. What process improvements are necessary for the Future State to become a reality?

QUESTION 1: WHAT IS THE TAKT TIME?

Takt time synchronizes the pace of the Value Stream to the pace of customer demand. One of the key wastes discussed in the Introduction is overproduction. **Overproduction** is:

- Making more than is required by the next process
- Making it earlier than is required by the next process
- Making it faster than is required by the next process

All of these conditions cause waiting, extra transporting/moving, extra motion, defects, and inventory!

Building to Takt time requires **system efficiency** — everything working at the same rate. An example of this would be a rowing team stroking in perfect harmony to someone's call or a drum. Many Value Streams today focus on **point efficiency** — every person/machine/process is working as fast and hard as possible individually. Imagine how fast the boat would go if each member of the rowing team just paddled as fast and hard as they could!

Question 1 Example

Continuing with the example Current State Value Stream Map from Chapter 3, the Takt time is:

$$\text{Takt Time} = \frac{\text{Available Time per Day (400 min.)}}{\text{Customer Demand per Day (100)}} = 4 \text{ min.}$$

Therefore, the Value Stream needs to build a unit every 4 minutes in order to keep pace with the customer needs.

QUESTION 2: BUILD DIRECTLY TO SHIPPING OR TO A FINISHED GOODS SUPERMARKET?

This question addresses whether we will hold, or accumulate, finished goods or ship finished product as it is produced. If the product is made to standard specifications, then it is possible to accumulate the different standard varieties (or mix) before shipping.

In some cases, holding some finished product can help smooth out variation in production volumes.

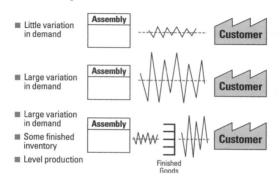

A **supermarket** is a location where a predetermined standard inventory is kept to supply downstream processes or Value Streams. Each item in a supermarket has a specific location, just like shelves in a supermarket (note the icon for supermarket). As an item is taken, a signal is given to provide more.

However, if the product is custom, or specific to a particular customer, it must be shipped as it is produced. All custom products and most service and transactional products would fall into this category. The only accumulation of product in this case is for shipping logistics — this can be a truck load or an electronic batch process that processes transactions.

Question 2 Example

If the Value Stream produces widgets A, B, and C, then we can accumulate extra widgets in a supermarket to ensure that shipment to the customer can occur regardless of which model they choose.

If the Value Stream provides a laundry service, the service of laundering your shirt requires that your clean shirt be shipped to you, not someone else. So, we cannot accumulate extra clean shirts in case yours doesn't get done on time.

QUESTION 3: WHERE CAN CONTINUOUS FLOW BE USED?

Continuous flow results when product is produced and moved from one process step to the next:

- One-at-a-time (as one unit has been defined)
- Without stoppages
- Without scrap
- Without backflow

The benefits of continuous flow include:

- Reduced lead times
- Lower costs
- Improved quality
- Additional stability and flexibility
- Reduced injuries
- Increased employee ownership through involvement

Discontinuous flow can be identified by:

- Inventory accumulation between processes
- Work processed in batches
- Process steps not close to each other
- Evidence of defects, rework, and scrap
- Excessive changeover time and other downtime
- Inconsistent output rates (hour-to-hour, shift-to-shift, etc.)
- Problems not addressed immediately or permanently
- Under- or over-utilized operators
- Imbalance in operator workloads

An **operator balance chart** (OBC) helps compare the process cycle time for each person to Takt time. This comparison is also made directly between process cycle times and Takt time. Let's call this a **process balance chart**. This is more appropriate when the cycle of a process depends on equipment as well as/instead of people to do the work. We will discuss equipment cycle time in a later chapter.

In either case, having a picture of how the Value Stream cycles compared to takt can help determine where continuous flow might be possible. Here's an operator balance chart for the example process:

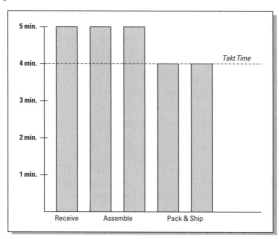

This operator balance chart tells us that Receive and Assemble cannot cycle within Takt and that Pack & Ship can barely cycle within Takt. Another way to measure the number of people required to cycle within Takt time is to use the formula:

$$\text{\# of People} = \frac{\text{Total processing time (23 min.)}}{\text{Takt time (4 min.)}} = 5.75$$

This calculation verifies that people are working overtime, or they are not able to produce at the rate that the customer needs.

Caution! Do NOT base the future design on this calculation. Improvements and allowances for variation need to be made before determining the number of people needed. The future state design is based on *product flow*, not keeping people busy.

Question 3 Example

In the example process, we can eliminate the time and cost of overproduction by connecting assemble with pack & ship in a continuous flow. We have also added a supermarket for finished goods assuming that we are producing widgets in three varieties.

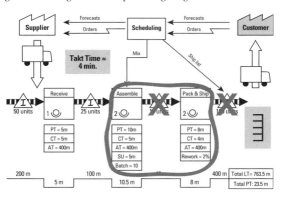

QUESTION 4: WHERE ARE PULL SYSTEMS NEEDED?

When continuous flow is not possible, use pull systems to limit and manage inventory, which improves flow and eliminates waste. **Pull** is a system in which work is done only in response to a signal from the customer or from a downstream process that indicates a need for more product. In some Value Streams, a pull system can also indicate what product is needed.

In any case, when no product is needed, production *stops*. We do not overproduce! This is one of the most difficult things to do — stop working to solve problems. A Japanese term often used to refer to this concept is **Jidoka**.

The benefits of pull include:
- Team ownership of the flow of product
- Visibility
- Simplicity
- Urgency created to solve problems
- Proper allocation of resources

Use a **supermarket pull system** to control production when continuous flow does not exist and the upstream process must still operate in a batch mode. Possible reasons for this are that the process:
- Operates very fast or very slow
- Requires setup for product variations
- Is too far away for one unit at a time to be realistic
- Has too much lead time
- Is too unreliable to link directly to another process

A **kanban** is a signal to produce more or withdraw items in a supermarket pull system. It tells us when, how much, and, possibly, what to produce. Below are some additional icons associated with supermarket pull systems:

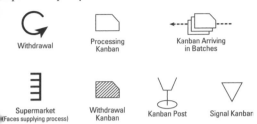

Withdrawal	Processing Kanban	Kanban Arriving in Batches

Supermarket (Faces supplying process)	Withdrawal Kanban	Kanban Post	Signal Kanban

This is how a supermarket pull system works:

- Customers take only what they need when they need it.
- Supplier produces to replenish only what was withdrawn.
- Defective product and incorrect quantities are never sent to the next process.
- Inventories are lowered by reducing the kanban quantity as problems are solved.

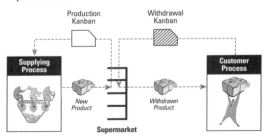

The supermarket should be kept as small as possible to facilitate flow. The supermarket size can be established by considering the usage rate, the refill move quantities, the refill lead time, and the minimum point to signal for more to be produced.

A **FIFO** (first in first out) pull system is used when it's not practical to maintain an inventory of all possible product variations due to having custom products, short shelf life products, or expensive and infrequently ordered products. The icon for a FIFO pull system is:

This is how a FIFO pull system works:

- Products are made-to-order while overall inventory is minimized
- The first product to enter the FIFO system is also the first one to exit
- Removal of one unit triggers the supplying process to produce more
- Often maintained with a lane or other visible method

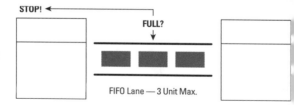

Question 4 Example

In the example Future State Value Stream map, we have shown the Assemble and Pack & Ship processes as one continuous flow process. This new process pulls from the supermarket, which is filled by the receive process. We have also targeted using a supermarket pull system for supplier materials and for finished goods.

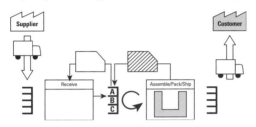

If this Value Stream provided a custom service, FIFO pull systems might replace supermarkets.

QUESTION 5: AT WHAT SINGLE POINT (THE PACEMAKER) IN THE VALUE STREAM IS PRODUCTION TRIGGERED?

The **pacemaker** is the one point that is scheduled in the Value Stream. The pacemaker sets the pace for the entire Value Stream. *It is controlled by the pace of customer needs and is NOT the bottleneck, or slowest process!* This is not what the Value Stream can now do, but what is needed to build at the customer's pace. This is where the drummer sits, using the earlier analogy of drumbeat to signal Takt time.

The pacemaker should be set as close to the customer as possible. However, service and transactional Value Streams typically require the pacemaker to be placed further upstream in the process.

Question 5 Example

In the example Value Stream, the new assemble/pack/ship cell can set the pace for the Value Stream. We have used a drum icon to indicate the pacemaker on the VSM.

QUESTION 6: HOW IS PRODUCTION MIX LEVELED AT THE PACEMAKER?

Production mix refers to the different varieties or types of products. The Lean principle is: make every product every day. The goal is to have a flexible and responsive Value Stream that can produce any variety that the customer needs. A supermarket pull system can facilitate leveling the mix, since it makes the variety of products visible and easier to manage.

And, as batch sizes are reduced and we get closer to one-at-a-time, our ability to make a particular product variety as the customer needs it increases. The Future State Value Stream mapping icon is:

Question 6 Example

In the example Value Stream, we should make some A's, B's, and C's each day versus making A's on Monday, B's on Tuesday, and C's on Wednesday, etc. This is how we might show this in the Future State Value Stream map:

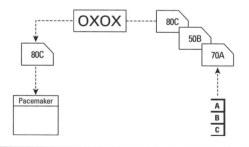

QUESTION 7: HOW IS PRODUCTION VOLUME LEVELED AT THE PACEMAKER?

Production volume is leveled at the pacemaker by producing to Takt time. Visual feedback is needed to determine how each process is performing to Takt time. In a custom order, service, or transactional Value Stream, each unit may take a different amount of work content. One option in this case is to set the demand calculation as a time increment of product instead of a unit. Then, different variations can be defined as certain time increments for the purpose of managing flow to Takt time.

However, if the Takt time is seconds or only a few minutes, feedback may come at such a fast pace that it's meaningless.

To establish a reasonable management/feedback timeframe, Lean uses a multiple of Takt time, or **pitch**. Pitch is often calculated using pack-out quantity, or pack size of finished goods. This is the amount of product removed for the customer at once. This could be a pallet of widgets, an order of laundry, or a batch run of transactions.

Pitch should be a reasonable time set to:
- Schedule and handle materials
- Monitor production
- Respond to problems

Question 7 Example

In the example Value Stream, let's assume that the average order size is 5 units. In this case,

Pitch = Takt time (4 min.) x 5 = 20 min.

Twenty minutes seems to be a reasonable timeframe to receive feedback on adherence to Takt time.

QUESTION 8: WHAT PROCESS IMPROVEMENTS ARE NECESSARY FOR THE FUTURE STATE TO BECOME A REALITY?

To make the Future State Value Stream map a reality, improvements in certain areas are required. Key improvements required are noted on the Value Stream map as Kaizen bursts. **Kaizen** is a Japanese terms for continuous improvement. The icon for a Kaizen burst is:

Question 8 Example

The example Future State Value Stream will require reducing processing times by eliminating waste as well as cross training so people can help out with different tasks. Other common improvements can include setup reduction, moving people and/or processes closer together, etc. Below is one version of a completed Future State Value Stream map. Note that the total lead time has been reduced from 763.5 minutes to 106 minutes!

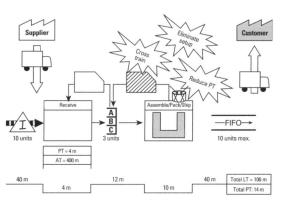

CONCLUSION

The Lean principles applied in this chapter are the essence of creating a Lean Value Stream. The next step is to begin an implementation plan to make the Future State Value Stream map a reality.

SELECTING THE RIGHT PROJECT TO BEGIN MAKING THE LEAN VALUE STREAM A REALITY

The Future State Value Stream map represents a new design for an entire Value Stream. In most cases, this is too much change for one effort, team or project. It is better to create projects that are manageable within this overall design and that can be completed in no more than six months. These are called **project "loops"** because we draw loops around different parts of the Future State Value Stream map.

The next steps are:
1. Identify project "loops" on the Future State Value Stream map
2. Prioritize those projects
3. Determine the timeframe for each project and the sequence for implementation
4. Complete project charter/s, assign team/s and get going

It may be possible to work on the different project "loops" simultaneously by coordinating different teams and efforts. Or, it may be necessary to work on one loop at a time.

CONTINUOUS FLOW CELLS

Since continuous flow is a primary goal of Lean, let's further define a continuous flow cell before identifying the project "loops."

A **cell** is an arrangement of people, machines, material, and methods with the processing steps placed right next to each other in sequential order, through which parts are processed one-at-a-time in a continuous flow. We get as close to one-at-a-time as possible — this may be a small batch that is consistently maintained through the sequence of processing steps. An example of an office cell is shown below.

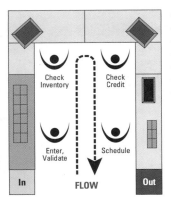

- Multifunctional
- Co-located
- One-at-a-time flow
- Standardized work
- WIP can be held constant
- Flexible work assignments
- Easy communications
- More efficient use of space
- Unbalanced operations are visible allowing for corrective action

STEP 1: IDENTIFYING THE PROJECT "LOOPS"

Identifying the project "loops" requires an understanding of the Future State design and the work that will be required to make it a reality. We have identified possible project "loops" for the example Value Stream below.

Note that four projects have been identified, each requiring certain knowledge, skills, and effort.

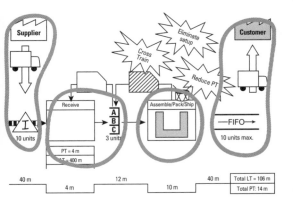

STEP 2: PRIORITIZING THE PROJECT "LOOPS"

There is no hard and fast rule for prioritizing the project "loops"; however, the following guidelines are recommended:

- Begin as close to the customer as possible to begin the pull from the customer and make improvements visible to the customer sooner.

- Focus on the pacemaker process, or cell, since this will set the pace to Takt time for the entire Value Stream.

- Work on the processes within your control before branching out to suppliers or customers; your internal work may change requirements.

- Learn as you go and apply what you learn; don't be afraid to revise the Future State design as you learn more.

- And, finally, ask the question: "Which loop has the best chance of making the greatest improvement considering the customer and the business?"

STEP 3: DETERMINING THE TIMEFRAMES

A review of the data collected may also uncover the need to collect or analyze additional data to determine project timeframes and sequencing. Key data to consider includes:

- The Product Family — confirm the products included
- The product volumes — understand fully all variations and trends, including how product mix is handled
- The information flows — What is it and how does it get communicated?
- The material flows — What are the materials used (can be information)? Where do they come from? How are they managed?
- The people — Who has what knowledge? Who provides indirect support?
- The physical flow (can be virtual — networks or systems) — review the Spaghetti Diagram, measuring distances and noting problems
- Metrics — How is the Value Stream measured? What measures can be used for the project "loops" identified?

The result of this analysis is an implementation plan. In the example Value Stream, we selected the continuous flow cell — Assemble/Pack/Ship — as the first project since it is close to the customer and the pacemaker.

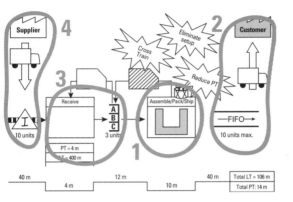

STEP 4: CHARTERING THE PROJECT AND SELECTING THE TEAM

Complete project charters should be done for each project (use other references for details on how to do a project charter). These include scope, timeframes, problem statements, goals, and measures. Team members for each project should be carefully chosen given the data from step 3. We highly recommend that there be some common team members for all projects within a Value Stream to ensure that the overall Future State design is implemented successfully.

CONCLUSION

This step in implementing Lean is critical to making the Future State Value Stream a reality — don't treat it lightly!

ANALYZING TIME AND WORK

A core pinrciple of Lean is to be synchronized with the customer. Takt time is the available time divided by customer demand. We want to build to Takt time in an even, balanced flow. Therefore, the work must be designed to cycle within Takt. In order to design the work, we need to analyze the work being done in the chosen project "loop."

TAKT TIME AND DAILY DEMAND VARIATION

Most Value Streams do not have a constant customer demand. If you are making widgets and have low daily variation in demand, it is possible to operate at a constant Takt time and meet demand with occasional overtime or a small finished goods inventory.

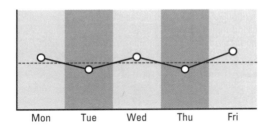

If you are making widgets and have a high daily variation in demand, it is possible to operate at a constant Takt time and meet demand with a larger finished goods inventory.

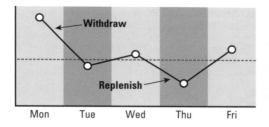

However, if your product is a custom widget, a service or a transaction, the daily demand can have high variation, but inventory cannot be used to buffer this variation. The options include varying available time or using a different Takt time each day.

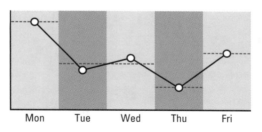

Another consideration is leveling the mix, or how to build every product variation every day. **Interval** is the elapsed time it takes to cycle through all products in the product family.

Batch Production

Run a large batch of Product A, then change to Product B, then to Product C. After all products are run, start over with Product A.

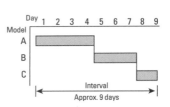

ANALYZING THE WORK

The next step is to analyze the work within the selected project "loop." **Work element** is the smallest increment of work that can be transferred from one person to another. The **work content** is the sum of all work elements to make one unit start to finish within the Project scope of the Value Stream. You will most likely be analyzing the work for one project "loop" at a time.

Breaking processes into work elements helps identify and eliminate waste and readjust workloads. In order to do this analysis we must:

1. Identify the work elements
2. Time each element

In identifying work elements, we will find **in-cycle work**, or the normal repetitive work elements required to perform the job and **out-of-cycle work**, or activities that do not occur every cycle. Examples of out-of-cycle work include replenishing supplies, getting tools, or stopping to check the schedule.

We will NOT include out-of-cycle work in the new cell. We will eliminate it, convert it to in-cycle work, or assign it outside the cell.

DETERMINING WORK ELEMENTS
1. Define the scope of work to analyze
2. Observe a qualified person to get a sense of the overall job
3. Observe several cycles, define each element and refine
4. Describe each element with a clear beginning and end
5. Record elements in the sequence they are done
6. Separate people and equipment activities
7. Identify and record out-of-cycle work

TIMING WORK ELEMENTS

Collect real times at the process using a qualified person (not necessarily the slowest or fastest) for each separate work element as defined above. Select the lowest repeatable time (mode), the average, or the median time. Choose which is most representative of the work element over time. Below is a process study form for one work element in the process Assemble:

Process	Work Element	1	2	3	4	Lowest Repeatable	Notes
Assemble	Attach Part A to Part B	.4	.5	.5	.5	.5	

IMPROVING WORK ELEMENTS

To begin analyzing and improving the work elements in the project "loop," create a **single stack** of all work elements required to make one unit. A single stack is a "stack," or list, of all work elements with the time for each. See the example below — a bar chart is frequently used to depict a single stack.

Next, create a **paper kaizen** for these work elements. This is a list of all work elements with improvements possible given the plan to create a continuous flow cell. Guidelines for creating a paper kaizen include:

- Do not include walking time
- Do not include out-of-cycle work
- If possible, convert out-of-cycle to in-cycle work
- Do not include time waiting for equipment — we will assume that people can do other tasks while equipment is working
- Do not include unload time if automated ejection could reasonably be used

See the single stack and paper kaizen example below. Note that the improvements shown are made by combining the two processes into one continuous flow cell as designed in the example Future State Value Stream map.

We have not rearranged any work elements yet! Nor, have we thought about distributing work elements to people.

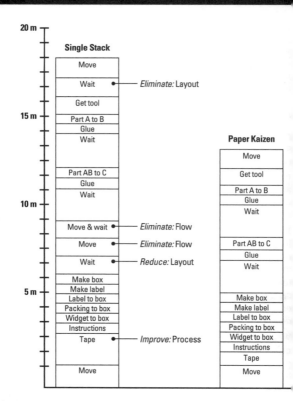

CONCLUSION

We have identified and improved the work to be included in the new continuous flow cell. Following the analysis of equipment in this workflow, we will be ready to design the new cell.

©2006 Rath & Strong/Aon Management Consulting

ANALYZING EQUIPMENT EFFECTIVENESS

Almost all Value Streams have some equipment — it may be heavy automatic equipment in a manufacturing process, light equipment manually operated, or a combination of computers, networks and printers in an office. So, ALL Lean implementations should include analyzing equipment as yet another factor in eliminating waste and increasing flow!

COLLECTING EQUIPMENT DATA

Since all processes must have the capability to cycle within Takt time, the cycle time of equipment is key. **Machine cycle** is the time required to produce one unit; it does not include load, start, and unload. Typically we use the machine cycle plus load and unload to test the capability to cycle within Takt, IF we are assuming that setup time is accounted for in extra inventory.

Effective machine cycle is the machine cycle + load/start/unload time + (setup time ÷ batch size). We use this measure to test the capability to cycle within Takt time when we are *not* assuming that setup time is accounted for in extra inventory. This decision should be based on how the future process will really run. *Note in the example below that machine 1 has the capability to cycle much faster than Takt. We do not want to do this since this would result in overproduction!*

When the capability to cycle exceeds Takt time, we have a **bottleneck**. Bottleneck refers to any condition where the cycle time of a process (automated or not) exceeds Takt time. In the example below, machine 3 is a bottleneck.

EQUIPMENT CYCLE VS. TAKT TIME

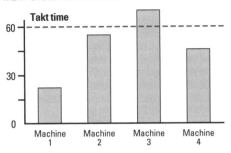

The **defect rate** is the total number of defects produced ÷ the total number of units produced. Again, this applies to any process.

Uptime is (scheduled hours − unplanned downtime) ÷ scheduled hours. This measure is usually associated with equipment and identifies the time that the machine/process really ran compared to the time planned to run.

STEPS TO COLLECT EQUIPMENT DATA

Below are steps to begin collecting data to analyze each piece of equipment within the cell:

1. Collect basic data as explained above
2. Determine if each has:
   a. Long setup time
   b. Chronic quality problems
   c. Excessive unplanned downtime
3. Calculate machine cycle and/or effective machine cycle

4. Evaluate the capability to cycle vs. Takt time
5. Identify approach for any bottleneck conditions
6. Determine whether needed equipment can be dedicated to the cell

WHAT IF A BOTTLENECK IS IDENTIFIED?

If bottlenecks are found, there are several things that can be done to reduce the effective machine cycle:

- Reduce setup times
- Improve load/start/unload times
- Reduce the machine cycle
- Move some of the work to another machine, or use two machines
- Duplicate the cell or decouple the machine from the cell and use pull
- Increase the available time and, therefore, the Takt time

GUIDELINES FOR EQUIPMENT IN THE CELL

- Plan the effective machine cycle to be no more than 80% of Takt time
- Avoid complex, large, multi-functional equipment resulting in higher cost per increment, less flexibility, and often less reliability
- Use simple, small, single-function machines which are less costly, more flexible, and have shorter cycle times
- Make setup time support an interval of one day or less (to support making every part every day) and less than one Takt time cycle at the pacemaker
- Avoid and/or reduce batching
- Design in maintainability

WHEN TO AUTOMATE

Note the diagram below that explains the levels of automation. The first thing to automate (in level 2) is the machine cycle itself. The second thing to consider automating is the unload process (level 3). There is a "great divide" between levels 3 and 4 in terms of technology required and cost to automate.

	Load Machine	Machine Cycle	Unload Machine	Transfer Part
1	Manual	Manual	Manual	Manual
2	Manual	Auto	Manual	Manual
3	Manual	Auto	Auto	Manual

"The Divide"

	Load Machine	Machine Cycle	Unload Machine	Transfer Part
4	Auto	Auto	Auto	Manual
5	Auto	Auto	Auto	Auto

Automation guidelines include:
- Introduce auto-eject whenever operators must use both hands to handle a part
- Install one-touch automation where possible
- Incorporate sensors to signal abnormal conditions and stop machines if necessary, so operators don't need to watch machines during their cycle

OVERALL EQUIPMENT EFFECTIVENESS

Measuring and analyzing equipment effectiveness reflects how well equipment is being utilized. This can help us improve productivity, flow, and quality by identifying key areas of improvement. Our goal in Lean is to balance equipment effectiveness with adherence to Takt time!

Overall Equipment Effectiveness (OEE) is a way to measure equipment based on the six losses (or wastes associated with equipment):

Downtime Losses (Availability)
1. Equipment failure (breakdowns)
2. Setup and adjustment

Efficiency Losses (Production Efficiency)
3. Minor stoppages
4. Reduced speed

Quality Losses (Quality Rate)
5. Defects
6. Reduced yield

$$OEE = AVAILABILITY \times EFFICIENCY \times QUALITY$$

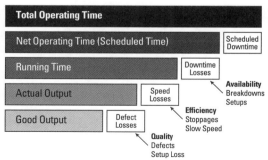

Total operating time = 24 hours, 7 days a week

Net operating time = total operating time – scheduled downtime

Running time = Net operating time – downtime losses due to breakdowns and setups

Actual output = Running time – speed losses due to stoppages and slow speed

Good output = Actual output – defect losses due to any defects and setup losses (product destroyed while setting up)

The goal for Lean is that equipment can produce good parts during at least 85 percent of *scheduled time*. As a rule of thumb, aim for at least:

- Availability: > 90 percent
- Efficiency: > 95 percent
- Quality: > 99 percent

CONCLUSION

Analyzing equipment effectiveness is important. The above highly-used model of OEE does not take into account the Lean principle of producing ONLY to Takt time instead of producing "as many as you can, as fast as you can." Therefore, this is a useful analysis only if we also consider adhering to Lean principles.

ANALYZING EQUIPMENT THROUGH TOTAL PRODUCTIVE MAINTENANCE

Total Productive Maintenance (TPM) is a company-wide approach for improving the effectiveness, longevity, and uptime of equipment. It was first introduced in the early 1970s and combined preventative maintenance practices, Total Quality Control (TQC) and employee involvement. TPM is critical to Lean because it attacks downtime and quality losses, both important wastes that can have significant negative impact on flow and lead time.

TPM also harnesses the efforts of all employees towards quality, safety, and efficiency. This part of TPM is often referred to as **Autonomous Maintenance** (AM) and will be discussed later in this chapter.

TPM AND LEAN

Reliable equipment is a Lean requirement!
- Lean's short lead times and minimal inventory require reliable processes, so equipment breakdowns and defects must be minimized
- Waste reduction in fixed assets requires equipment to run at the rate needed, when needed, without producing defective parts
- Lean projects expose equipment reliability issues and improvements deteriorate if these issues are not addressed

THE TRANSITION TO TPM

From:	To:
Breakdowns are inevitable	"Zero Breakdowns" is possible
Wait until they break	Predict and prevent problems
Order parts when needed	Critical spare parts inventory
Inadequate attention to preventive maintenance	Computerized Maintenance Management System
No operator involvement; clear division between Production and Maintenance	Operators have skills to inspect equipment, assist with diagnosis, and make some repairs

THE 5 PILLARS OF TPM ARE:

Pillars	Description
Eliminate the big six losses	Improve equipment effectiveness as measured by OEE
Autonomous Maintenance	Operator involvement in maintaining and improving equipment performance
A planned maintenance system	Improve the use of preventative maintenance practices
Improve equipment and maintenance skills	Improve the skills of operators and maintenance personnel
Mistake-proof design and early equipment management	Design equipment that requires less maintenance and manage the startup of new equipment

TPM seeks to reduce or eliminate lost operating time due to the six big losses:

1. Equipment failure, or breakdown
2. Setup and adjustment
3. Minor stoppages
4. Reduced speed
5. Defects
6. Reduced yield and startup loss

ARE BREAKDOWNS INEVITABLE?

The answer should be: "No!" in a Lean environment. Poor maintenance and incorrect operation cause deterioration leading to defects and eventually breakdowns. It has been said that over 50 percent of all breakdowns are the result of contamination and lack of lubrication alone!

All equipment eventually wears out no matter what we do. **Natural deterioration** causes losses due to normal wear and tear over time when equipment is used and maintained correctly. **Accelerated deterioration** occurs at a faster rate due to neglect or faulty methods, leading to breakdowns and shorter useful life of equipment. You will see on the chart below that Autonomous Maintenance addresses accelerated deterioration.

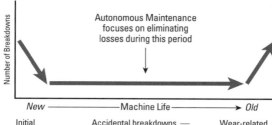

Follow these three steps to prevent breakdowns:

1. Maintain the normal condition of equipment

   a. Daily cleaning, checking, lubrication, tightening

   b. Use and operate machines correctly

2. Discover abnormalities before they cause problems

   a. Daily checking and familiarity with the equipment

   b. Over time, learn and document the right things to check and the right way to check them

   c. Periodic diagnostic tests by maintenance technicians

3. Respond quickly to abnormalities

   a. Restore the equipment to normal condition promptly before it causes a problem or breakdown

AUTONOMOUS MAINTENANCE

Autonomous maintenance (AM) harnesses the efforts of all employees towards quality, safety, and efficiency. Recognizing the limitations of some companies to involve employees in this way, this is still a valid and important topic for your Lean implementation. The idea here is to at least have those who are using equipment recognize when something is different before a problem develops.

■ Cleaning becomes inspection

■ Inspection reveals abnormalities

■ Abnormalities can be restored or improved

■ Restoration and improvements produce positive results

■ Positive results lead to pride in the workplace and provide a foundation for further improvement

THE 7 STEPS TO IMPLEMENT AUTONOMOUS MAINTENANCE ARE:

Step	Description
1. Initial Cleaning	Remove contaminants and unneeded machine parts; discover hidden problems
2. Eliminate sources of contamination	Eliminate sources or prevent accumulation, improve accessibility to machine
3. Cleaning and lubrication standards	Develop cleaning, lubrication, and inspection standards for daily or periodic use
4. Inspection skills training	Learn how to do a thorough inspection; learn how to make simple repairs
5. Autonomous Inspections	On-going inspections; refine standards, make machine improvements
6. Organize the Workplace	Broaden scope of activities: standardize control over tooling, dies, etc.; address other losses; collect data
7. On-going AM; advanced improvement activities	Continuous improvement activities, skills development, integrate with company goals

HOW AUTONOMOUS MAINTENANCE CONTRIBUTES
TO SAFETY

Below is how the steps to implement Autonomous Maintenance contribute to safety. Safety is an important topic in any environment, regardless of the limitations in involving employees in new tasks.

AM Step	Eliminate Unsafe Conditions
1. Initial Cleaning	Correct problems with moving parts
2. Eliminate sources of contamination	Correct problems with harmful substances, machine guards
3. Cleaning and lubrication standards	Develop and review work standards based on safe practices
4. Inspection skills training	Check and improve performance of safety devices and equipment
	Eliminate Unsafe Behavior
5. Autonomous Inspections	Correct stressful methods
6. Organize the Workplace	Assure workplace organization
7. On-going AM; advanced improvement activities	Motivate eveyone to participate in maintaining the workplace

CONCLUSION

Total Productive Maintenance including Autonomous Maintenance should be incorporated into every Lean cell design to ensure that equipment *always supports* product flow to Takt time.

ANALYZING EQUIPMENT SETUP

Setup is the act of changing from one job or type of job to another. Since effort and time are usually required to make this change, setups tend to be done infrequently, and, therefore, work gets done in large batches.

We tend to think of setups in manufacturing Value Streams, but setups also exist in service and transactional Value Streams as a result of machine-related issues (i.e., loading a different software program) or external requirements ("We only do applications on Thursdays").

Other terms often used for setup include changeover and SMED (Single Minute Exchange of Dies). The *why*, *what*, *who*, and *how* of setup reduction will be discussed in this chapter.

WHY REDUCE SETUP TIME?

The following five reasons for reducing setup time are discussed in more detail in subsequent sections.

1. To reduce the interval, improving responsiveness and flexibility

2. To reduce inventory by reducing batch sizes

3. To improve quality, standardizing the process and reducing variability

4. To make the setup easier to do, simplifying steps and fixing problems

5. To recover capacity, saving time to produce more product

Of course, eliminating setups gives us the opportunity to create true continuous flow. This is the ultimate solution!

REDUCING THE INTERVAL WITH SETUP REDUCTION
Interval is the time it takes to cycle through all the product variations (mix or models) in a Product Family. Traditionally, each variation is produced in large batches to avoid setups.

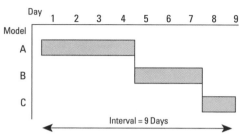

In a flexible Lean Value Stream, every variation is run every day, or better yet, several times during each day.

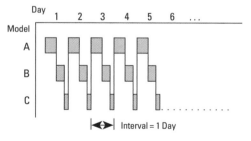

REDUCING INVENTORY WITH SETUP REDUCTION
When setup time is reduced, setups can be done more frequently without increasing costs. This will reduce batch size, and therefore inventory, while increasing flexibility.

Note in the example below that a 4-hour setup is required to produce 100 units. If we can reduce the setup to 1 hour, 25 units at a time can be made for the same total cost. There is a direct relationship between the setup time and the batch size.

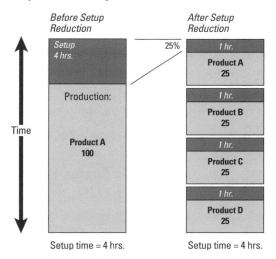

IMPROVING QUALITY WITH SETUP REDUCTION

In order to reduce setup time, variability must be reduced or eliminated in the setup methods and the material being produced. Anything else that contributes to post-setup adjustments must also be eliminated. And, "practice makes perfect," so by doing more setups more often, the setup is standardized even more.

MAKING SETUPS EASIER WITH SETUP REDUCTION

The improvements that make setups quicker invariably also make them easier to do through:

- Simplified procedures
- Easier physical tasks
- Fewer tools
- Better workplace organization
- Fewer adjustments
- Standardized methods = same way every time

RECOVERING CAPACITY WITH SETUP REDUCTION

Reducing setup time will free up time that can be used one of two ways:

1. Setup more often with smaller batches — this is the Lean approach
2. Produce more product during the time saved with reduced setup time — this is a cost-savings approach if more capacity is really required; however, larger batches inhibit flow!

WHAT IS SETUP REDUCTION?

The idea behind setup reduction is not to "hurry up" to get the setup done faster. It is to simplify the setup making it easier to do while working at a normal pace.

The setup redesign process consists of the following steps:

1. Analyze the way the setup is currently done
2. Eliminate what can be done before or after the setup
3. Fix recurring problems
4. Simplify what remains

HOW IS SETUP TIME MEASURED?

Setup time is measured as total elapsed time from the last piece of the prior job until normal production rate is reached on the new job.

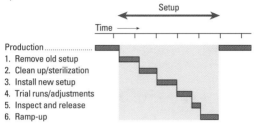

Production.......................
1. Remove old setup
2. Clean up/sterilization
3. Install new setup
4. Trial runs/adjustments
5. Inspect and release
6. Ramp-up

KEY DRIVERS OF SETUP TIME

Key drivers of setup time are teardown/cleanup, new setup, and adjustment.

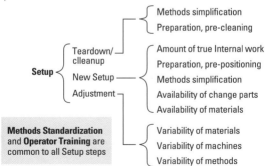

Setup
- Teardown/cleanup
  - Methods simplification
  - Preparation, pre-cleaning
- New Setup
  - Amount of true Internal work
  - Preparation, pre-positioning
  - Methods simplification
  - Availability of change parts
  - Availability of materials
- Adjustment

Methods Standardization and **Operator Training** are common to all Setup steps
- Variability of materials
- Variability of machines
- Variability of methods

RESULTS OF SETUP REDUCTION

Typical results of a setup reduction effort like the one being described in this chapter would be a *75 percent reduction in the setup time* (if this process has not been applied within two years). This is assuming a low cost/no cost approach!

Setup reduction supports a Lean implementation and makes a good case for changing traditional thinking about setups:

- It's OK for each operator to do it their own way
- No two setups are done the same way
- Each shift readjusts the previous shift's setup
- "Somebody else does setups, it's not my job!"
- "The longer the setup, the better the quality"
- "If there were a better way we'd already be doing it!"
- "If it works, don't change it"

WHO DOES THE SETUP REDUCTION?

Setup reduction efforts are *NOT engineering projects*. The experts who actually do the work need to be involved, and they must have the necessary support from supervision, maintenance, engineering, scheduling, etc. Setup reduction is a team effort!

HOW IS SETUP REDUCTION DONE?

The methodology for reducing setup time includes the following steps:

1. Select the setup and the team
2. Establish the baseline:
   a. Videotape and document the setup
3. Analyze the baseline
   a. Categorize steps as internal or external
   b. Further categorize internal steps

4 . Improve the setup:
   a. Convert internal steps to external
   b. Simplify internal steps
   c. Eliminate adjustments
   d. Solve other problems and streamline external steps
5. Pilot the new methods
6. Document the new methods; train employees

HOW TO ANALYZE AND IMPROVE THE SETUP

The first step in improving the setup is to categorize steps as **internal** or **external**. Internal steps can be performed only when the equipment is stopped, and external steps can be performed while the equipment is running even if they are not done that way now.

Then, categorize each internal step as attachment, adjustment, or problem. Attack attachments and problems first; this may eliminate some of the adjustments, and adjustments are more difficult to solve.

Next, finalize the rebalancing of workloads. And, finally, simplify the external work. This does not affect setup time, but will reduce cost.

A roadmap of this process is shown on the following page:

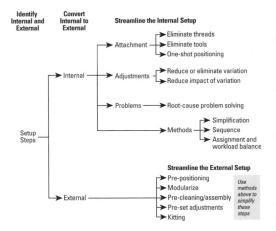

CONCLUSION

Setup impacts Flow and Lead Time as well as flexibility. Therefore, setup analysis and reduction is key in implementing Lean principles in any Value Stream that has setups and/or batches.

CREATING A CELL LAYOUT FOR ULTIMATE FLOW

We have calculated Takt time, analyzed the work, analyzed equipment within the selected project "loop," and defined and improved work elements. We are now ready to begin designing the continuous flow cell layout.

Note once again, that the cell will be designed for ultimate product flow. *Designing what the people and/or equipment do in the cell will follow a completed detailed cell layout.*

We will do this in three steps:
1. Develop a concept layout
2. Develop a materials plan
3. Develop a detailed layout

STEP 1: DEVELOP A CONCEPT LAYOUT
The final step in improving the work content will be to develop an **ideal sequence** for the work elements. We improved the single stack by doing a paper kaizen in chapter 6.

DEVELOPING AN IDEAL SEQUENCE OF WORK ELEMENTS
Now, the order in which the work elements are done is analyzed for improvement. As work elements are re-sequenced, we inevitably will find additional improvements to be included in the ideal sequence. We then use this ideal sequence of work elements to begin designing the cell layout concept.

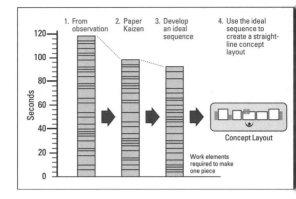

Ideal Sequence Example

Opportunities were found for re-sequencing in the assemble/pack/ship example paper kaizen. The chart below reflects the idea of doing both assemblies before gluing them at the same time and, therefore, having to wait only one time for the glue to set. We also eliminated time from get tool with the assumption that an improved layout will make the tool easier to retrieve.

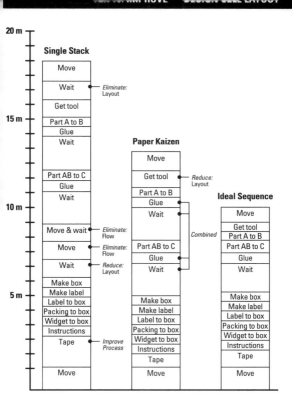

STEPS TO DEVELOP THE CONCEPT LAYOUT

The **concept layout** is developed by following these steps:

1. Start with your ideal sequence of work elements

2. Make a straight-line concept layout to ensure uni-directional flow

3. Design for "one operator processing one piece" to ensure that the product flow is good

4. Determine how parts will be presented to the operator

5. Traditionally, subassemblies are produced independently of the cell, building in batches and inventory:

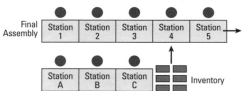

Instead, we want to integrate off-line subassemblies so they produce at the same rate and mix as the cell:

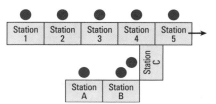

6. Walk through each work element and motion

7. Apply Motion Economy and Ergonomic principles (see Chapter 14 for more information)

   a. Reduce the number of motions

   b. Perform motions simultaneously

   c. Reduce the distance of each motion

   d. Make motions easier

8. Use the walk through to refine the work sequence

Concept Layout Example

Below is a concept layout for the example cell:

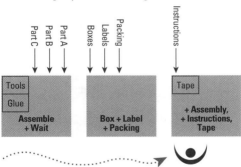

STEP 2: DEVELOP A MATERIALS PLAN

A materials plan should answer the following questions:

- What parts/supplies are involved?
- How will they be handled (racks, containers, etc.)?
- How will they be replenished?
- How much WIP should we plan in the cell?
- What will happen to the empty containers?

USING AN ASSEMBLY CHART TO CLARIFY THE WORK

An assembly chart is a very useful way to create a picture of the way that the cell will use the materials required. It shows what parts are involved, where they are used, the order in which they have to be used, and possibly where we have options to make changes.

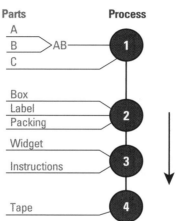

HOW TO DEVELOP A PLAN FOR EVERY PART

A **plan for every part** (PFEP) can then be developed showing all relevant data, such as usage per day, quantity and size of containers, and how much we need at the cell at one time (or, how often we need replenishment). Below is an example of a PFEP.

PLAN FOR EVERY PART EXAMPLE

| Part # | Description | Use/Day | Standard Container | | | | | No. of Cards |
			Qty.	L	W	H	Wgt.	
3482	A	100	50	15"	10"	6"	5#	4
6593	B	100	50	12"	9"	4"	12#	2
4518	C	100	200	48"	9"	9"	15#	6

MATERIAL HANDLING CHECKLIST

Guidelines for handling materials include:

- Materials should be close to where they will be used giving operators an opportunity to use both hands simultaneously to retrieve them.

- Replenishment of materials should be done with kanban without interrupting the people doing the work

- Containers for materials should be designed to help the people using them, not the material handlers or suppliers

- Work-in-process inventory should be limited to a minimum manageable quantity, and extra inventory should not be stored in or near the cell so that people are tempted to stop to get more material

COMPLETING THE MATERIALS PLAN

And, finally, develop a complete materials analysis and plan that is clear and easy to follow. The plan should address how, where, and who will manage materials in the cell. And, once again, pictures are better than words!

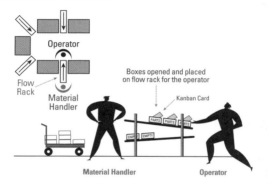

Material Handler   Operator

STEP 3: DEVELOP A DETAILED LAYOUT

The concept layout is converted to scale, and equipment is configured to the desired arrangement. Next, the layout is refined using the cell layout guidelines below. Finally, the material handling process is designed to present materials without interrupting the work in the cell.

CELL LAYOUT CHECKLIST

Guidelines for cell layout include:

- Place steps (equipment and workstations) close together with no obstacles in walking paths and no places for inventory to accumulate
- Place the first and last steps close together to facilitate flexibility, communication, and product flow; this is often referred to as a "U-shaped" design
- Segregate automated and manual steps to allow flexibility in distributing the work
- Support flexibility with physical designs (utility drops, workstations on wheels, etc.)
- Dedicate tools, place them close and orient them for use
- Make safety and good ergonomics a primary concern for the entire cell, including materials handling
- Include equipment guidelines (chapter 7)

Detailed Cell Layout Example

Note that we have wrapped around the concept layout to form a detailed layout per the checklist above.

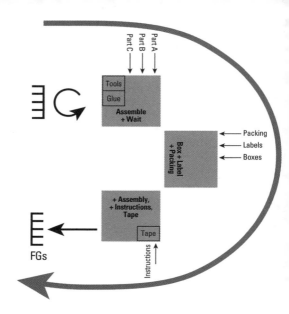

REFINING THE LAYOUT

The next steps are to:

1. Draw the operator walking pattern to test the flow

2. Pantomime the operator motions to ensure good ergonomics

3. Refine the layout as necessary

CONCLUSION

A detailed cell layout has been developed using the concept layout, and incorporating and staffing the materials, cell design, and equipment guidelines. Additional work on work elements is required before finalizing this design.

STAFFING A CELL TO MEET TAKT TIME

Now that the cell has been designed to operate with a varying number of people, we need to determine the actual number of people needed in the cell, what each will do, and how the work will get done. The design will then be tested to determine if changes in demand for the product can be met.

This is necessary at this stage of cell design to ensure that our design can handle the people needed to produce what the customer needs when the customer needs it.

HOW MANY PEOPLE ARE NEEDED?

We calculated the number of people needed to cycle within Takt time for the current state by dividing the total work content by Takt time. Now the work content has been improved by doing a paper Kaizen and an ideal sequence, and the flow has been greatly improved by doing a cell design layout.

At this point, we need to allow for people variability that will inherently occur due to minor stoppages, fatigue, and variation in work content. We call this **planned cycle time** (PCT) and recommend that it be 85 percent – 95 percent of Takt time.

However, you will need to determine this percentage based on past history, company agreements and policies, and other relevant factors. This is NOT an allowance for equipment downtime, setup time, or quality variations! This is for people variations.

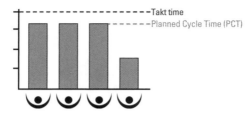

The calculation for the number of people in a cell is:

$$\text{Number of people} = \frac{\text{Total Work Content*}}{\text{Planned Cycle Time}}$$

* work content for ideal flow

The calculation for the number of people based on the ideal sequence from Chapter 10 follows. We have chosen to use 90 percent of Takt time for planned cycle time in the example.

$$\frac{\text{Total Work Content}}{\text{PCT} = \text{Takt Time} \times .90} = \frac{10 \text{ m}}{4 \text{ m} \times .9} = 2.8 \text{ people}$$

WHAT TO DO WITH PARTIAL JOBS?
Then, the question arises:

What should we do with the .8 operator?

First, let's consider Lean thinking as opposed to traditional thinking. Traditionally, we have spread the work evenly among people to balance the work. However, Lean encourages us to fully load each person and expose the waste, or extra capacity, to focus on continuous improvement.

The guidelines for partial jobs are:

Fraction of person in calculation	Guideline
< .3	Do not add an additional person. Instead, further reduce waste and business value work
.3 – .5	Hold off on an additional person for a week or two in order to evaluate if enough waste and business value work can be removed to eliminate the need for an additional person
> .5	Add a person, but continue efforts to reduce waste and business value work in order to eventually eliminate the need for the person

DISTRIBUTING THE WORK

There are many options for distributing the work among the people — this is a good time to be very creative in brainstorming the different ways that work might be distributed. Any idea should be tested as completely as possible before locking in a plan. This test may have to be done with models and/or pantomiming.

Splitting the Work

One example might be to split the work so that the people are each cycling between two workstations.

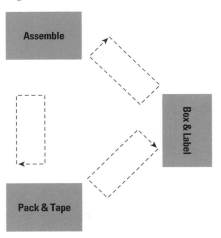

Cycling through the Work

Another example might be to have each person cycle through all workstations one after the other; or, you can reverse the flow and have each person begin at the end of the process (this requires inventory between each workstation).

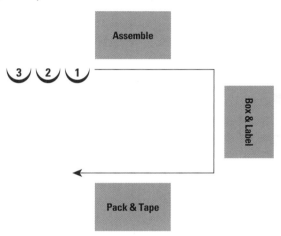

Dedicating Workstations

A third example might be to have one person at each workstation. Of course, this only works when the number of people required equals the number of workstations.

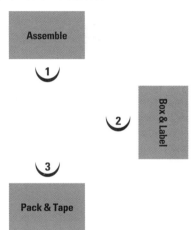

DOCUMENTING THE WORK

The work sequence must be documented clearly. An operator balance chart can be used, or possibly a **standard work chart** that combines the work elements, the time for each work element, the walk distance, and a picture of the cell layout to show where each work element occurs.

Standard Work		Product: Widget	Date:
		Process:	Takt Time:

	Work Element	**Work**	**Walk**	
1	Move	1.0	10'	
2	Get tool	.5		
3	Part A to B	.5		
4	Part AB to C	.5		
5	Glue both	.5		
6	Wait	2.0	3'	
7	Make box	.5	1'	
8	Make label	.5	1'	
9	Label to box	.5		
10	Packing to box	.5	1'	
11	Widget to box	.5	3'	
12	Instructions	.5	1'	
13	Tape	1.0		
14	Move	1.0	4'	

Another example of a way to document clearly what is happening in the cell when there is a combination of people and equipment is a **combination chart**. This chart shows the time cycles for each as well as walking time. See the example below using a shirt laundry cell. This is the short folding process, which has machine and manual steps.

	Work Element	Manual	Machine	Walk	Operator Machine 0	5	Seconds 10	15	Takt 20	Repeat Sequence 25
3	Fold machine (4)		30							
4	Make box (per 6)	3		1						
5	Box	6			Walk					
6	Attach order	5			Walking not required					
1	Move	5		2						
2	Place on machine	17								

Operator #1 can't do next element because operator's time would exceed Takt time. This element would be given to Operator #2

CHANGING THE DEMAND

We have designed our cell for an average or median demand level. Now we need to determine how to respond to changes in the demand level.

Short term, we may:
- Use a finished goods supermarket to absorb fluctuations
- Use overtime or bring in part time people

Long term, we will need some combination of:
- Planned overtime (increases available time)
- Additional people (spreads work content)
- Additional cells

USING PLANNED OVERTIME

In order to calculate planned overtime, we need to base our calculations on planned cycle time:

	Required Production	PCT	Required Time (sec)	Equiv. Hours	Planned OT
Forecast	120	3.6 m	432 m		
Current	100	3.6 m	360 m		
Difference			72 m	1.2 hr.	1.0 hr.

- Required Time = Required Processing x Planned Cycle Time (Takt time x .90)
- Subtract current Available Time from Required Time
- Convert difference in time into hours; round to a reasonable increment of planned overtime

CHANGING THE NUMBER OF PEOPLE

Changing the output of the cell by changing the number of people working in the cell is often referred to as **toggling**. The different settings (number of people) are like the settings on a toggle switch.

The goal of Lean is to keep the work content for each person very close to Takt time and have each person produce about the same amount of product. This is referred to as **labor linearity**. We can ask the question (and, therefore, calculate the results) two different ways:

1. How many people do I need for my peak output and for my slowest output?

2. How many can I produce with one more person or one less person?

Let's answer each of these questions using our example cell.

How Many People Are Needed?

To calculate the number of people needed for a different demand, we must recalculate Takt time since demand is part of the Takt time formula. Let's say that we want to know the number of people required to build 130:

$$\frac{\text{Available time} \quad (400 \text{ m})}{\text{Demand} \quad (130)} = 3.1 \text{ m Takt time}$$

Then, we can recalculate the number of people:

$$\frac{\text{Work content} \quad (10 \text{ m})}{\text{PCT} = \text{Takt time x .9} \quad (2.8 \text{ m})} = 3.6 \text{ people}$$

Since this is greater than .5, we would most likely add a fourth person to our cell. We'll need to go back and determine how work would be distributed with four people in the cell — this may require some redesign.

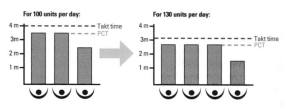

The same process can also be used to determine the number of people for a reduced demand.

Checking Labor Linearity

If we are producing 100 with 2.8 people, this equals 35.7 units per person. If we are now producing 130 with 3.6 people, this equals 36 units per person. So, the labor linearity checks out.

HOW MANY CAN I PRODUCE?

If the number of people is toggled by one (can be in either direction), how many can I produce? We can use the same two formulas to calculate this by applying simple algebra to rearrange the formulas using the data that we have. Follow these steps to answer the question using the example cell and subtracting one person to equal 1.8 people versus 2.8:

1. Solve for the new PCT by rearranging the formula for calculating the number of people:

$$\frac{\text{Work content} \quad (10 \text{ m})}{\text{Number of people} \quad (1.8 \text{ m})} = 5.6 \text{ m PCT}$$

2. Solve for the new Takt time:

$$\frac{\text{PCT} \quad (5.6 \text{ m})}{\% \text{ used} \quad (.9)} = 6.2 \text{ m Takt time}$$

3. Solve for the new demand by rearranging the formula for Takt time:

$$\frac{\text{Available time} \quad (400 \text{ m})}{\text{Takt time} \quad (6.2 \text{ m})} = 64.5 \text{ units Demand}$$

So, we can build 64 units with 1.8 people within Takt time (or PCT), or 35.5 each. The labor linearity calculation confirms our answer since it is approximately the same number of units per person as before.

REFINING THE CELL LAYOUT

All valid staffing options must be tested with the cell layout design to ensure that they are doable. *It is likely that some adjustments will be needed*. In some cases, the answer will be to duplicate the cell and plan to run all cells only part of the time.

CONCLUSION

We have now determined the staffing required to meet customer needs, and we have taken into account the variations in customer demand that inevitably occur. We have also explored different ways to distribute the work within a cell. It is critical to test the cell design layout again after completing these steps and to adjust the design if required. We will now explore more ways to improve our cell design before proceeding to mockup.

STANDARDIZING FOR FLEXIBILITY

Work must be standardized before flexibility can exist. If the way we do work is constantly changing with no standards, implementing Lean will result in chaos. Standardizing for flexibility may sound like an oxymoron, but actually standard work is necessary to achieve the ultimate flexibility required for great customer service.

Standard Work must be a part of every cell design!

WHAT IS STANDARD WORK AND WHY IS IT IMPORTANT?

Standard Work is work done the same way each time, producing the same outcome each time. Documentation is necessary as a means of achieving standardization; but, on its own, documentation will not achieve standardization.

Standard Work is visual; it is NOT documentation in a file or drawer or stored away electronically. The ultimate test of whether a cell has an adequate level of Standard Work is for someone to be able to perform the work correctly using ONLY the Standard Work in the cell.

Standard work originated during and after World War II at Toyota. A great need to rapidly train unskilled workers led to having the workers write their own work instructions. They learned that these instructions can't just be written at a desk or by an engineer because you work them out by trying them.

WHY IS STANDARDIZATION IMPORTANT?

- Process consistency

  When a process is stabilized, the effects of human variability are minimized.

- Process improvement

  Standardization provides a baseline, or foundation, for improvement. This supports a data-based approach such as DMAIC versus just tinkering with the process.

- Training

  Standard work provides a base for consistent training, eliminating the variation that typically occurs and speeding up effectiveness of training.

- Visual control

  When done correctly, Standard Work is visual, which helps distinguish between normal and abnormal methods.

- Safety

  Unsafe practices are formally eliminated from the process.

THREE AREAS OF STANDARDIZATION

In practice, three areas of work need to be standardized:

1. Activities of individual people, known as **Standard Work 1**

2. Connections, or the customer and supplier relationships in the process, known as **Standard Work 2**

3. Pathways, or the ways that materials and services are provided, known as **Standard Work 3**

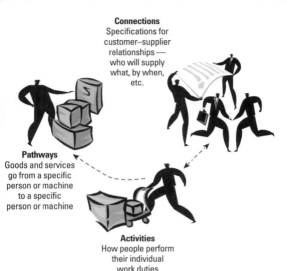

Connections
Specifications for customer–supplier relationships — who will supply what, by when, etc.

Pathways
Goods and services go from a specific person or machine to a specific person or machine

Activities
How people perform their individual work duties

STANDARD WORK 1 — INDIVIDUAL WORK

Standard Work 1 consists of a precise description of each work activity specifying data such as lead time, cycle time, Takt time, sequence of activities, materials/information necessary, quality requirements, etc.

Each activity is highly specified and includes:

- Content — specific tasks and how they should be performed
- Sequence — the order in which the tasks should be performed
- Timing — the time allowed for each task and the total time for the assigned work

Standard Work documentation does not have a set format. Different kinds of processes and tasks require different forms. Each company should have a consistent way to document work. The important thing is not the format, but the effectiveness of the Standard Work. However, don't forget that pictures are worth a thousand words!

Ohno at Toyota believed that the people who do the work should write their own work instructions because:

- They are the "experts" in their job
- They will rarely follow instructions written by a staff person that they don't fully understand
- To support a particular way of doing something, they will need to understand why it is important
- Thinking about their work and why things need to be done in a certain way is the first step in involving them in continuous improvement
- They will keep their work instructions simple and make them understandable to co-workers

Depending on skill and experience, Standard Work may be written by Value Stream Leaders, Value Stream Leaders jointly with employees, or by employees on their own. Coordination is necessary between shifts and with upstream and downstream processes to ensure that the Value Stream is optimized, not just one area at the expense of others.

Standard Work should be easily changed as improvements are identified. Some companies provide time each week for employees to stop producing product and update their Standard Work documentation.

Standard Work may be changed when:

- Schedules change

- Mix of work changes

- Problems are resolved

- Improvement ideas are implemented

Any of these conditions could easily require a change in Takt time, which will require changes in work assignments and work sequences.

STANDARD WORK 2 — CONNECTIONS

Standard Work 2 defines the relationship between each internal customer and supplier as to what will be provided, how, and when. The objectives are to make the customer/supplier interactions more predictable, driving variability out of the Value Stream.

It consists of:

- A concise agreement developed jointly by internal customers and each supplier regarding the quantity, quality, condition, and timing of the work to be passed between them

- A simple, visual method based on pull for the customer to request work from the supplier

- A plan for regularly auditing the agreement

STANDARD WORK 3 — PATHWAYS

Standard Work 3 deals with the ways that material, service, or information is provided. The objective is to drive out variability from the Value Stream resulting from multiple providers and complex pathways. This will eliminate confusion and guesswork regarding the flow of work.

Standard Work 3 consists of:
- Defining a specific pathway for each product
- Defining a specific supplier for each product
- Providing a means to evaluate performance over time

STANDARD WORK AND IMPROVEMENT
There can be no improvement without Standard Work! When normal and abnormal work activities are undifferentiated, waste almost inevitably occurs. Standard Work provides a basis for continuous improvement.

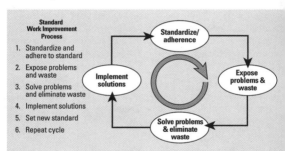

Standard Work Improvement Process
1. Standardize and adhere to standard
2. Expose problems and waste
3. Solve problems and eliminate waste
4. Implement solutions
5. Set new standard
6. Repeat cycle

The process to create Standard Work is:

When	Who*	What
Cell Design	Team	Create initial Standard Work; refine it as the design of the cell evolves
Mock-up	Team and employees	Revise Standard Work as needed
Debugging	Team and employees	Further refine Standard Work as problems are solved or improvements are made
Production	Team and employees	Restudy the work at the end of the Debugging period and finalize Standard Work
Approvals	Team	Cell leader and people should formally sign off on the final Standard Work
On-going	Team Leader	Audit employees; ensure that Standard Work is kept up to date. Team leader may do the updating or, once employees are trained, assign updating to them.

* This process assumes that Team Leaders are on the cell-design team

The steps in developing Standard Work are compared below to the steps in cell design:

Cell Design Stage	What
Single Stack	The "single stack" is the first stage in developing the overall sequence of work elements; it becomes the foundation of Standard Work.
Layout	The ideal sequence of the concept layout is a refinement of the single stack. This will be further refined as the detailed layout is developed.
Work Distribution	Initial Standard Work can be developed once the number of people has been determined and the method of work distribution established. The ideal sequence may be modified in the process of assigning work elements. An initial set of Standard Work documents should be prepared for the volume variations identified.
Mock-up	The Mock-up process should include a thorough review of the Initial Standard Work.

CONCLUSION

Standard Work is a vital piece of any initial cell design and of the ensuing ongoing continuous improvement efforts. *It is never complete!*

MAINTAINING ORDER THROUGH 5S AND VISUAL WORKPLACE

The ultimate goal in a Lean Value Stream is to have a workplace that is:

- Self-explaining
- Self-ordering
- Self-regulating
- Self-improving

The design of any cell, or process in general, should include the above. In other words, there are visual cues and practices in place as a part of the design that ensure consistency and order.

You will see throughout this discussion that 5S and visual workplace principles apply to electronic work as well as physical work.

Visibility can be a poster or electronic sign in the workplace or a message or sidebar on a computer screen for electronic processes. Be creative in making your visual workplace effective!

5S — WHAT, WHY, AND HOW

5s is a process to:

- Create workplace *organization* and *standardization*
- Achieve and sustain a clear, clean, safe and organized workplace
- Ensure that the workplace contains only what is needed, when it is needed, and where it is needed

WHAT IS 5S?

The 5S's consist of:

1. Sort: necessary versus unnecessary
2. Set in order: a place for everything
3. Shine: clean and ready to use
4. Standardize: maintain the gains
5. Sustain: self-discipline

The 5S circle below sums up 5S with benefits in the outer circle.

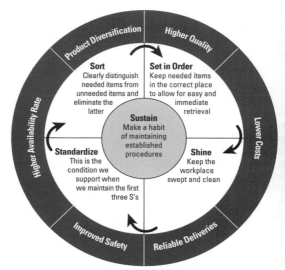

Step 1: Sort

The underlying concept of **sort** is that unnecessary equipment, material, and supplies clutter the workplace, causing unnecessary work and motion, making it more difficult to find items that are truly needed, and sometimes making the work area less safe.

Sort also applies to electronic work. Think of all those unneeded records and e-mails that clutter computers and servers! This clutter slows down electronic systems and causes extra time and effort to be spent finding electronic files that are needed.

Don't forget to pay close attention to safety hazards as you complete the steps in sort:

1. Discard anything that isn't needed.
2. Determine a quantity needed and location for anything that is definitely needed.
3. Place items being questioned in a **red tag holding area**
4. Resolve red tag items.

A red tag holding area is an area set aside to stage items in question. It should be out of the work area (and, out of sight). This process allows time for proper evaluation and disposition of items deemed to be unnecessary. Items are tagged with a red tag that provides pertinent information about the item (such as the category of item, what it is, where it came from), the quantity, the value, the originating date, and the eventual disposition of the item.

The idea is to get the items out of the work area to see if work can be done without them. Usually, the items are never missed! After a specified period of time, they can be discarded.

One caution, however, is: *keep in mind when the item is typically used and make sure that it is held through that period of time.* For instance, if something is generally only used during the holiday rush, make sure that it is kept through one holiday season to ensure that it's not needed before discarding the item.

If an item is disposed, determine if it's a capitalized asset and follow company procedure if it is. You will need to obtain approvals from appropriate people, such as the Value Stream Leader, manager, and financial person. Then, determine the method of disposal. Options can include re-use elsewhere, sell it, donate it, or scrap it.

Step 2: Set in Order

The underlying concept of **set in order** is to have a place for everything and everything in its place. Everything moveable or electronic should have a designated place to be when not in use. This place should be visual, and it should be obvious when the item is not in its place.

Set in order also applies to electronic work. Have you ever wasted time just looking for certain files on a computer? Protocol is needed for filing electronic records just as we have always needed for physical records.

The steps to implement set in order are:
1. Arrange items so they are easy to find, use, and put away.
2. Apply organizing concepts.
3. Use elimination techniques.
4. Create visual controls.

For items to be easy to find, use and put away, establish dedicated locations for each item that are well-marked and easy to access. Once again, don't forget about safety! Safety equipment should always be well-marked, in designated areas and fully operational.

Store most frequently used physical items close-at-hand:
- Above knees, below chest
- In a location that does not disrupt the natural rhythm of the task
- Obtainable with minimum body motion
- Always in the same place so no time is wasted searching

Most frequently used electronic items should be easily accessible through special start-up programs or short cuts.

Organizing concepts include:
- Suspension:
  - Suspend tools from above, within reach of the user, using a retractable cable or balance device. This will eliminate the need to return a tool as well as the chance of misplacing it.
- Incorporation:
  - Tools and devices are smoothly integrated into the work process and are stored where they are used so there is no need to return after use.
- Elimination:
  - Finding a way to provide the function of the tool without actually using it.

Elimination techniques include:

- Tool unification
  - Combining the function of two or more tools into one tool
  - Example: standardize all fasteners (flat or Phillips head)
- Tool substitution
  - Using something other than the tool to provide the tool's function
  - Example: replace hex-head bolts with butterfly-grip bolts
- Method substitution
  - Replacing one method for another to improve efficiency
  - Example: use pins or clamps instead of bolts

Visual controls are devices which inform or indicate a condition at a glance. For example, floor painting can indicate location or labeling can indicate identity. And, of course, color coding is widely used, but only works for those of us who can see colors! *So, always offer an alternate identification technique for color coding.*

The following example of a tool board illustrates how visual controls can help make items easy to find, use and put away.

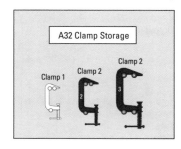

The designated location for Clamp #1 is outlined on the tool board. This makes it easy to:

- Determine if it is currently in-use by someone else
- Put away when not in use
- See if tools have been put away in a wrong location

This concept is more challenging to implement in electronic processes, but certainly not impossible.

Step 3: Shine

The underlying concept of **shine** is to have everything clean and ready to use. *This implies that items are cleaned after use and put away clean and ready to use again.*

Shine has some application in electronic processes if we consider "cleaning up" electronic records. An example might be updating information and discarding old information within electronic records.

The steps to implement shine include:

1. Establish a **five-minute shine** routine: a small block of time each day to focus on housekeeping.
2. Develop **housekeeping checklists** consisting of shine activities that include who, when and what area plus columns for weekly and monthly assessments.
3. Establish ongoing and specific inspection routines and provide a process for easily logging all requests for maintenance with a space for date resolved.

For each of the above steps, develop a plan that includes the following components:

Targets	Identify tools and equipment in the workplace that need to be included in the Shine process; determine cleaning and inspection frequency for each item
Schedule	Develop a schedule and responsibilities; allocate regular time for Shine activities
Methods	Develop standard methods for what will be done, how it will be done and when. Incorporate inspection methods as these are developed and as cleaning becomes a routine
Tools/supplies	Identify required tools and supplies and ensure that they are available
Implement	Carry out methods per the standards and schedule; audit effectiveness

Step 4: Standardize

The underlying concept of **standardize** is to maintain the gains. So, once the above three components of 5S are developed and tested successfully, we need to continue doing the established process. This can be the most difficult part of 5S!

Standardize is best accomplished by using aids to control what happens, when it happens, and how it happens and then focusing on prevention, or making it difficult (if not impossible) to do it wrong.

The steps to implement standardize are:

1. Design Cells with 5S in mind
   - Design for Sort: find ways to prevent items from accumulating in the workplace
   - Design for Set-in-Order: make it difficult or impossible to put things back in the wrong place
   - Design for Shine: prevent things from getting dirty by treating contamination problems at the source

2. Make 5S a habit
   - Assign 5S job responsibilities
   - Integrate 5S duties into regular work duties
   - Check the maintenance of the 5S duties

The key to sustain is *measurement*. Visible measures posted for inspection results, schedules, and 5S checklists are necessary to standardize 5S.

Step 5: Sustain

The underlying concept of **sustain** is self-discipline and motivation. There needs to be an awareness and focus on 5S with a rewards and recognition system in place. This will result in employee satisfaction and enthusiasm for continuing the 5S efforts.

If 5S is a part of a Lean cell design, the measures for 5S are incorporated into the measures for cell performance. In any case, checklists are required for compliance, and employees must be trained to ensure a full understanding of the 5S concepts and procedures.

5S AND CELL DESIGN

5S fits with cell design principles, and an effort to implement 5S as a part of creating a cell can be fun and energizing for employees.

The following chart shows how 5S should be integrated into cell design:

	5S as an integral part of Lean
Sort	"Paper Red Tag" before cell layout
Set in Order	Incorporate into the cell layout design process; implement with cell installation
Shine	Assess equipment before cell installation; carry out as a part of cell installation
Standardize	Incorporate into standard work for the cell
Sustain	Tie to cell performance

EXAMPLE OF 5S CHECKLIST

The following chart shows the progressive levels of 5S with some descriptors of each level. The key is to begin now implementing 5S — it is a critical component of every Lean implementation.

	Sort	Set in Order	Shine	Standardize	Sustain
Level 5 *Focus on Prevention*	Employees are continually seeking improvement opportunities	Documented method developed to provide continual evaluation, and process in place to implement improvements	Dependable, documented method of preventative cleaning and maintenance	Everyone continually seeking elimination of waste with changes documented and information shared	General appearance of a confident understanding of, and adherence to, the 5S principles
Level 4 *Focus on Consistency*	Dependable, documented method to keep the work area free of unnecessary items	Dependable, documented method to recognize visually if items are out of place or exceed quantity limits	5S agreements understood and practiced continually	Substantial process documentation available and followed	Follow through with 5S agreements and safety practices evident
Level 3 *Make It Visual*	Unnecessary items removed from workplace	Designated locations marked to make organization more visible	Work and break areas plus equipment cleaned daily; Visual controls established and marked	Working environment changes documented; Visual control agreements established	5S agreements and safety practices developed and utilized
Level 2 *Focus on Basics*	Necessary and unnecessary items separated	Designated locations established for items	Work and break areas cleand on a regular schedule; Key items to check identified	Methods are being improved, but changes haven't been documented	A recognizable effort has been made to improve condition of the workplace
Level 1 *Just Beginning*	Needed and not needed items mixed throughout the workplace	Items are randomly located throughout the workplace	Workplace areas are dirty, disorganized, and key items not marked or identified	Workplace methods are not consistently followed and are undocumented	Workplace checks are randonly performed and there is no visual measurement of 5S performance

CREATING A VISUAL WORKPLACE

A **visual workplace** makes it easy to:

- See the flow of work
- Understand the goals and how we stand in achieving them
- Train employees
- Identify problems

Examples of a visual workplace include:

Use different colors
to identify orders received
on different days of the week

Limit Size of Inbox
to Standard WIP or
eliminate inbox completely

Limit (electronic) queue
sizes to a minimum

Use Dashboards to
display Incoming Volumes

In a visual workplace, the:
- Productivity objective must be *visible*
- Current quality levels must be *visible*
- Work instructions must be *visible*
- Improvement strategy must be *visible*
- Customer satisfaction level must be *visible*

Visibility can be a poster or electronic sign in the workplace or a message or sidebar on a computer screen for electronic processes. Be creative in making your visual workplace effective!

CONCLUSION

5S makes sense. The issue is to DO IT and KEEP DOING IT! Visual controls are key to sustaining 5S.

IMPROVING ERGONOMICS
FOR HEALTH AND SAFETY

Ergonomics is a science addressing human performance and well-being in relation to the job, equipment, tools and the environment.

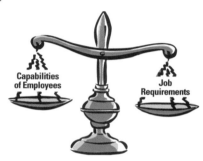

When implementing Lean principles through cell design, we simply want to be able to recognize an injurious situation in a current or new design and get ergonomic help when needed. *We are not providing enough information here to make you an ergonomics expert or practitioner!*

Signs that you may need ergonomic help with a cell design are that job tasks are uncomfortable, painful, or causing injury or lack of performance.

WHAT IS ERGONOMICS?

We will focus on two aspects of ergonomics:

- **Anthropometrics** is the analysis of body size and proportion in relation to the physical environment (for example, workstation, equipment, tools).
- **Biomechanics** is the analysis of body movements and the forces acting against those movements.

ANTHROPOMETRICS

There is a great deal of variation in both size and capability among the people in any population, and any population consists of many sub-populations (gender, age, ethnicity, occupation, etc.). Therefore, the average person doesn't exist!

The usual design approach is to design for the segment of the population that is between the 5th and 95th percentile when assuming a generally normal distribution. Remember that percentiles are specific only to the populations and the specific dimensions they describe.

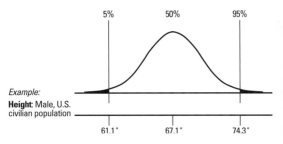

Example:
Height: Male, U.S. civilian population

The design approach suggested is to:

- Provide adjustability whenever possible; examples include workstation or chair height.
- Design for the extremes (5th or 95th percentile); examples include designing clearances for large people and reaches for small people.
- Design for the average (50th percentile) if adjustability is not practical; an example is door handle height.

BIOMECHANICS

We typically look at biomechanics in four categories:

- Hand/wrist
- Shoulder/neck
- Back/torso
- Legs/feet

Ergonomics Principles

The ergonomic principles for biomechanics include:

1. Reduce harmful positions; an example is bending or kneeling to do a task.

2. Reduce repetition rate by redesigning the work or rotating the tasks; an example is typing on a computer for long periods of time.

3. Minimize static positions in non-neutral positions. This includes isometric positions where very little movement occurs; examples include cramped or inactive postures, prolonged standing or sitting and sedentary work.

4. Reduce excessive force; an example is designs that use knees or back to apply pressure or force.

MOTION ECONOMY

The chart below provides a checklist for our cell design. The four basic principles of motion economy are:

1. Reduce the number of motions.
2. Perform motions simultaneously.
3. Reduce the distance of each motion.
4. Make motions easier.

Basic Principles	Motion	Work	Tools	Improvement
1. **Reduce the number of motions**	Both hands move symmetrically	Place tools and materials in order of use	For simple operations, or those requiring power, use devices operated by foot	Eliminate searching, choosing, carrying, placing, deliberating, and re-grasping
2. **Perform motions simultaneously**	Both hands start and finish at the same time	Design layouts so that both hands move simultaneously	Use devices for holding goods for a long period of time	Eliminate waiting, balancing, holding
3. **Reduce the distance of each motion**	Eliminate unnecessary movements	Place tools and materials to facilitate their use	Use appropriate containers for parts	Facilitate grasping and assembling
4. **Make motions easier**	Reduce the number of movements; combine movements where possible	Minimize the work area without obstructing body movements	Use fixing devices with fewer nuts and bolts	Reduce arm motions

CONCLUSION

The health and safety of people is paramount in redesigning the way that we do work. Include the ergonomics principles mentioned here in your cell design. However, before a full implementation is done, ask an ergonomics expert to evaluate the way that you intend to do work in the new design before proceeding. Adjust the design according to this evaluation as required.

MISTAKE-PROOFING THE IMPROVEMENTS

Mistake-proofing is making it easy to do right and impossible to do wrong. This is the ideal; however, making it nearly impossible or more difficult to do something wrong is a step in the right direction. We want our cell design to be as close to the ideal as possible.

Mistake-proofing is the use of low-cost devices or techniques to perform 100-percent inspection as a means of eliminating defects. It assumes that even the most conscientious and well-trained employee will occasionally make errors.

Mistake-proofing prevents errors from becoming defective products as one part of a larger inspection system.

HOW MISTAKE-PROOFING SUPPORTS LEAN

Lean and continuous flow depend on 100-percent quality. Defects cause delays, longer lead times, and extra inventory — all wastes. Mistake-proofing makes quality a part of the process instead of steps in the process (for inspections and rework).

Another term used for mistake-proofing is **Poka Yoke**. This is Japanese for: "to avoid inadvertent mistakes." *The goal for mistake proofing in Lean is to design processes and procedures so that mistakes are prevented, or, at the very least, detected right after they occur.*

135

MISTAKE-PROOFING PRINCIPLES

There are at least five mistake-proofing principles to remember when designing a new cell and/or process:

1. Control upstream, as close to the source of the defect as possible.

2. Establish controls appropriate to the severity of the potential defect.

3. Don't over-control — strive for the most efficient and economical control method.

4. Develop mistake-proofing cooperatively with operators, technicians, and engineers.

5. Don't delay improvement by over-analyzing.

DIFFERENT TYPES OF INSPECTION

The traditional approach to inspection has been to find defects. This has usually been based on sample inspections and acceptable quality levels (AQL's).

The Lean approach to inspection is to *prevent* defects by inspecting at or near the source. The objective, based on 100-percent inspection, is to detect and correct.

The four types of inspection include

1. **Final inspection**: output inspected at end of process
   • Defects can get to customer
   • Feedback and corrective action too slow to be effective

2. **Successive inspection**: each person inspects 100 percent of the work of the previous person before doing own operation
   • Can only check 2 or 3 characteristics
   • Must provide quick feedback and stop the flow to correct
   • Potential problems between workers

3. **Self inspection**: people inspect 100 percent of their own work
   - Defects discovered at origin allowing faster feedback and quicker corrective action
   - People may not always be objective; best used for objective characteristics
   - Must limit number of characteristics checked

4. **Source inspection**: process inputs are inspected to discover errors in conditions that lead to defects
   - Can take action to correct errors before they produce defective product
   - Sources of errors can include people, material, machines, methods, or information

MISTAKE-PROOFING TECHNIQUES

Mistake-proofing utilizes one of three techniques: physical characteristics, constant value, or process sequence.

Physical characteristics of a product are used to detect whether it is the correct part and/or placement. A plug configured for correct polarity is a good example of both.

Constant value is used when there is a "correct" answer for comparison. Examples might be the number of steps in a process (counting) or specific edits in a software program (input only a weekday that is not a holiday).

Process sequence is used to determine that the right steps have been completed in the right order. Checklists and sensors to check steps and sequence are good examples of this technique.

MISTAKE-PROOFING METHODS

Whether for manufacturing or service or electronic (transactional) processes, mistake-proofing methods share several common features:

- Either warnings that indicate the existence of a problem or preventative controls that stop the process until the problem is resolved
- Applied as source inspection to prevent errors from occurring or as self or successive inspection to detect errors that have just occurred
- Meant to be used by the front-line employees
- Typically low cost methods

In service processes, mistake-proofing interactions with customers focus on prevention.

An example of a warning method would be the spell-check feature in word-processing programs on your computer. This feature immediately notifies you if a word is not recognized by underlining the word and/or sounding a beep. However, it is still your choice whether to change the spelling or not.

An example of a preventative, or control, method is the fueling area of your car:

1. Filling pipe insert keeps larger, leaded-fuel nozzle from being inserted
2. Gas cap tether does not allow the motorist to drive off without the cap
3. Gas cap is fitted with ratchet to signal proper tightness and prevent over-tightening

Control methods are more powerful and should be used whenever possible.

MISTAKE-PROOFING STEPS

The steps to apply mistake-proofing are:

1. Identify the problem.

2. Identify the cause of the problem.

3. Determine at what level you can inspect the process (source, self, successive) If self or successive, strive over time to find a way to prevent the problem through source inspection.

4. Determine the mistake-proofing technique (physical characteristics, constant value, or process sequence).

5. Determine the method, or level of regulation (control or warning).

6. Design and implement a mistake-proofing process.

7. Try it out; refine it as necessary.

8. Train others.

9. Monitor results.

CONCLUSION

Mistake-proofing is a powerful methodology that should be used for every new cell or process design. Creativity and employee involvement can make mistake-proofing fun and more effective in ensuring that your cell is defect free.

USING KAIZEN WORKSHOPS FOR QUICK FOCUSED IMPROVEMENTS

Kaizen is the philosophy that continuous improvement takes place through small, incremental process improvements, repeated over and over again. A **Kaizen Workshop** is a short (3–5 days typically) event with intensive focus on one area of improvement. This is a participative event, involving ideally the people working in and supporting the area being improved.

THE WHAT, WHY, AND WHEN OF KAIZEN WORKSHOPS

WHAT IS A KAIZEN WORKSHOP?

The idea is to focus full time for a short period of time on a certain improvement, such as the Kaizen bursts noted on a Future State Value Stream Map. Results are actually achieved, and the workshop team gains new skills in applying Lean to achieve results.

Below is a comparison of a Kaizen Workshop to a Lean project:

	Project	Kaizen Workshop
Scope	Broad, negotiable; supports project loop from Future State Value Stream Map	Narrow, fixed; supports Value Stream Plan Kaizen bursts
Duration	Weeks or months	3–5 days
End point	When goals are achieved	Implemented changes
Team	Operators + Support	Operators + Support
Team size	Max. 8 people	Max. 8 people
Training	Team + technical skills	Limited + on-the-job training
Participation	Part-time for several months	Full-time for 3–5 days
Analysis	Developed by team	Prescribed
Focus	All phases of project	Detailed design and implementation

To have a successful Kaizen Workshop, certain conditions need to be in place. *Not all improvement efforts are appropriate for this format,* but you should consider the power of a Kaizen Workshop for those that do meet the conditions listed below:

- There is a willingness to improve and a belief that improvement is possible.
- Participants are able to work effectively in a group and everyone participates.
- The group has authority to accomplish the goal; an approval process is in place for implementation.
- Everyone is considered equal during the workshop — no level and status.
- The process can follow the structured approach of DMAIC.
- The workshop deliverables are documented.
- There is a process in place to standardize and further improve the solutions over time.

WHY USE A KAIZEN WORKSHOP?

Kaizen workshops are used to:

- Get quick results
- Provide focus on making concrete improvements
- Build enthusiasm by achieving results quickly
- Develop ownership for the solution through involvement

WHEN SHOULD A KAIZEN WORKSHOP BE USED?

Kaizen Workshops are not for every situation, and it can be detrimental to an effort to use a Kaizen Workshop in the wrong situation and not get the desired results. The following criteria should be met before considering a Kaizen Workshop:

- The event has a limited scope and clear boundaries.
- Necessary data can be gathered and available before the workshop.
- Results can be easily seen and measured.
- Resources can be freed up for the time required and are available for follow-up activities.
- The participants can bring about the changes needed, and the process owner is willing to decide on the spot (or very quickly).
- Interference with the current process can be managed.
- Support resources will be available.
- Employee involvement is desired.
- There will be follow-up after the workshop.

If these criteria cannot be met, it doesn't mean that you don't have a great project; it just means that a Kaizen Workshop may not be the way to proceed. Typical great projects for a Kaizen Workshop include: setup reduction, 5S, create standard work, or eliminate one well-defined defect. All of these are for one process or area only.

Do not use a Kaizen Workshop for measurement, analysis, or headcount reduction.

HOW TO PREPARE FOR AND RUN A KAIZEN WORKSHOP

STEP 1: IDENTIFY THE OBJECTIVES

A "mini" charter, or Kaizen charter, should be developed to identify the scope, objectives, and the team for the workshop. This Kaizen charter is specific to the workshop, but should tie right back to the overall Value Stream project charter. It should be clear how this effort fits into the larger effort chosen earlier as the project loop. The Kaizen charter should:

- Define the workshop scope.
- Set measurable goals for the workshop.
- Establish a timeframe for the workshop, the results and any follow-up required.

STEP 2: IDENTIFY THE WORKSHOP LEADER

The leader of a Kaizen Workshop should be knowledgeable and experienced in implementing Lean. This person needs to have strong leadership and facilitation skills, since you are trying to get a lot accomplished in a short period of time. They should have lots of energy, be very organized and have a bias for action.

STEP 3: IDENTIFY THE TEAM

The team will use Lean principles and tools with the assistance of the leader to analyze the data and determine solutions. They will implement those solutions as they are approved by the process owner and take on responsibility for follow-up actions. And, possibly most important, they will communicate the results of the workshop in their area, acting as a spokespersons and ambassadors for the team and for Lean.

Team members should be selected based on their:
- Experience and knowledge in the area
- Openness to change and willingness to experiment
- Credibility in the area — somebody colleagues listen to and whose opinion they respect
- Ability to influence others

We recommend that the team have appropriate people from the area being worked on, the right support people and staff for that area, and possibly one person not familiar with the area to help question the status quo.

STEP 4: PREPARE FOR THE WORKSHOP

The workshop leader must now prepare for the workshop with help from others in the area of focus. They need to:
- Ensure that all data required is collected, verified, and organized for analysis by the team.
- Invite participants and notify or confirm with their management.
- Line up the support resources — the people who will be needed to get the desired results; they need to be on standby and able to react quickly during the workshop.
- Prepare introduction and training materials.
- Ensure that all facilities, materials, etc. are scheduled and prepared.
- Schedule the process owner and other management for kick-off, review, and approval sessions during the week (a minimum of one meeting per day)

STEP 5: THE WORKSHOP

The kick-off presentation should include:

- Introductions
- Overview of the overall Value Stream charter, the project loop, and the Kaizen charter
- Q & A with the process owner and management
- Kaizen Workshop process overview with a suggested agenda
- Roles and responsibilities
- Review of available data

Training can occur up front, or you can use just-in-time training in small segments as needed. The team does need to have an understanding of Lean and some of the Lean tools before proceeding too far.

Depending on the number of days for the workshop, an agenda should be set according to the DMAIC methodology:

Define: Done ahead of time and reviewed Day 1

Measure: Done ahead of time and reviewed Day 1–2

Analyze: Some work done ahead of time, but the team gets very involved here Day 2–3

Improve: The team determines solutions, mocks up, debugs, and implements Day 3–4

Control: The team determines metrics and a plan to ensure that the solution is sustained and that continuous improvement will occur Day 3–5

A review/approval meeting needs to be scheduled with the process owner and other management at the end of each day. These final decision makers must be available to make decisions on the spot in order to avoid delaying the team!

Progress should be tracked continuously comparing the baseline data to where the team is in achieving the goals. A visible team scorecard can be updated so that everyone knows where they stand at all times.

STEP 6: PRESENT FINAL RECOMMENDATIONS

You may have made many incremental decisions during the week, but this is the final overall plan presentation to the process owner and management. For each change, consider presenting the following information:

- Define the issue being addressed
- Explain the proposed solution
- Outline the estimated benefits in applicable terms (financial, service, employees, etc.)
- Explain the resources required to implement
- Identify an owner for this solution to ensure that one person has the responsibility to see it through

All changes will be visibly tracked against a due date for the final implementations.

STEP 7: CELEBRATE!

Taking time to celebrate will pay off many times in generating interest and enthusiasm for future Kaizen Workshops and improvement projects in general. Celebration can take on many forms. However, it needs to provide an effective reward and recognition within your environment.

CONCLUSION

Kaizen Workshops can get those "Kaizen bursts" done quickly and generate a lot of enthusiasm for Lean and for improvement projects in general. Our only caution is to only use these workshops when the required conditions can be met.

PLANNING, IMPLEMENTING, AND DEBUGGING IMPROVEMENTS

Now that we have applied Lean principles and tools to the Value Stream project loop, we need to plan, implement, and debug our improvements. *Doing these steps well can make or break any effort, no matter how perfect the new design is!*

PLANNING FOR IMPLEMENTATION

To have an effective implementation plan, we need to make certain that our design is complete. We recommend a walk-through of the entire scope to ensure that everyone involved understands how the new cell will run considering items such as layout, responsibilities, Takt time, pitch, how demand will be signaled, and how variation in demand will be met.

DEVELOPING MEASUREMENTS TO GAUGE SUCCESS

One of the most important things to develop at this stage is how the performance of the cell will be measured. This is paramount because *you get what you measure — every time!*

There are different levels of measurement to consider. Both process measures and results or performance measures are important. As you can see on the chart below, **process measures** are measures within the process to give us immediate feedback on specific areas within the process. These measures are necessary as we are fine-tuning a new design and some of them may or may not be long-term measures.

Performance measures tend to measure what the customer of the process experiences, or results. These measures are more global (lead time of the Value Stream, versus processing time for one process) and tend to be longer-term measures of how the new cell is performing.

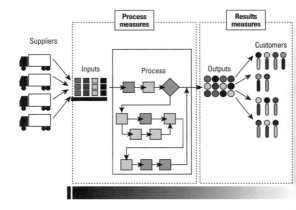

At this stage of the project, measures should tie back to the goals in the project charter as well as any other specific measures identified as being important. Three key points about determining measures are:

1. Fewer is better
2. They must be easily reported so that status can be understood at a glance
3. They must identify problems or problem areas to facilitate further improvements

DEVELOPING AN IMPLEMENTATION PLAN
The stages of implementation are shown below. Notice how the operator involvement increases as implementation is completed. **Implementation** begins at the mock-up stage. This is when we begin to actually set up the new cell.

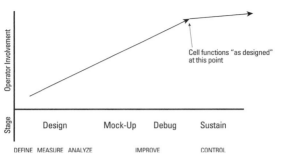

An **implementation plan** should be developed that shows the steps, or tasks, who is responsible, the status, the when it is due. A simple Gantt chart works for most cell implementations. However, if there are dependent tasks involved, you may want to use one of the more project management software packages.

Our approach is to keep it *simple* and *visible!* This requires updates to the plan to be easy.

DEVELOPING A MOCK-UP OF THE NEW DESIGN

The next step is to do a mock-up. A **mock-up** is a model of the new cell created to explain the design to the people who will run and support it and to find further improvements before full implementation. This is the step when the cell design begins to move from paper to reality.

A mock-up session includes a description of the project, the objectives, and the steps used in developing the new cell design. The design and the implementation plan is communicated to everyone involved in the mock-up.

The session also includes a thorough walk-through where the operators of the cell can go through the motions of running the cell using a conference room mock up, cardboard cut-outs, or actual (or identical) equipment arranged per the cell design.

After the Mock-Up

There are several steps that should be taken after the mock-up session:

1. Document and consider all suggestions from the mock-up.

2. Decide which suggestions should be incorporated into the final design.

3. Get final approval for the design.

4. Update everyone involved in the mock-up, including feedback on all suggestions — not just those implemented.

5. Proceed with pre-implementation items such as training, physical space, and getting needed equipment and supplies.

IMPLEMENTING IMPROVEMENTS

Now it is time to actually implement the cell design, making the cell a reality. If it is possible to take small steps instead of "jumping in all at once," we highly recommend this approach. We refer to these small but real steps as implementing a **pilot**.

A pilot might be running only one product or one type of product in the cell to begin with. Then, as the design is confirmed, other products or product types are added until it is fully operational. Or, a pilot might be implementing one of several like cells before implementing all of them.

In any case, be ready to make on-the-spot adjustments in layout and design as you implement.

DEBUGGING THE DESIGN

Debugging may be the most important part of implementation. The debugging stage begins with start-up and goes to running per the cell design (includes volumes, mix, people, support systems, and additional improvements).

The cell is usually started up gradually, or in phases. Suggestions for improvement are noted and should be implemented before the next day. *This requires a very rigorous reaction and support system.* Debugging usually takes several weeks. One guideline is:

- After 1 day, the cell might be at 60 percent of target
- After 1 week, the cell might be at 80 percent
- And, after 2 weeks, the cell might be at 90 percent

The point here is: *Don't expect the cell to run per the design and plan right away!*

Another fact to remember is: *During any change process, things always get worse before they get better!*

In the chart below we assume that the Value Stream would have continued to run at status quo with no changes. However, with our new cell design, we expect the improvement noted in distance (B). We must expect and plan for the drop from status quo early in our implementation. The goal is to shorten the time indicated by (A) and make (B) as large as possible.

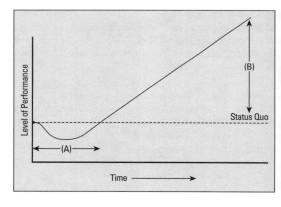

USING VISUAL MEASURES TO IMPROVE

A problem awareness board like the one shown below tracks the cell's adherence to plan (or Takt time) and logs problems that may have been encountered. This type of visual measure should be visible to everyone in the cell; and, as we said before, a support plan needs to be in place to solve these problems.

This type of visual measure is useful not only during implementation and debugging, but also when the cell is fully operational.

Per Day: 690			Takt time: 40 sec.
Time	Plan	Actual	Problems
7–8	90	90	
8–9	90	83	Bender downtime (electrical)
9–10	75	59	Bender downtime (cont'd.) Crimping quality
10–11	90	86	Out of parts (ferrules)
11–12	15		

Hourly plan vs. actual; could also track cumulative plan vs. actual

CONCLUSION

Planning, implementing, and debugging are critical steps in actually reaping the benefits of the work done to apply Lean principles and create a new design. Don't take this step lightly — it is a "make or break" step.

MAKING CHANGES A WAY OF LIFE

In order to make the changes a way of life, two things must happen:
1. Maintain continuous improvement.
2. Close the project effectively, and determine what's next.

MAINTAINING CONTINUOUS IMPROVEMENT

Several methods exist for maintaining and sustaining continuous improvement. We will discuss three:
- Detecting and responding to problems quickly
- Audits
- Process analysis

In order to detect and respond to problems quickly, the process owner along with the support staff and the people in the cell need to:
- Detect problems quickly.
- Respond to problems rapidly.
- Implement improvement ideas overnight.
- Update and create standard work for the cell and for support to the cell.

An auditing process can prevent backsliding and keep improvement going. A cascading system of audits keeps the focus on the cell and is a part of management's standard work. This process is taught by each level to the next level.

For instance, people in the cell audit daily while management might audit weekly, and the general management monthly.

A monthly process analysis can also be used to ensure continuous improvement.

The process owner might ask:
- What interrupts the flow?
- What wastes still exist?
- What is the next level of improvement?

Then, they identify:
- What works well
- What needs to be improved

And, finally, they
- Discuss findings with the people in the process
- Decide what improvements to make
- Quickly implement the selected improvements

CLOSING A PROJECT SUCCESSFULLY

Each project needs to have a clear ending when results are assessed, lessons are learned for the next time and responsibility for continued operation and improvement of the cell are clearly owned by the Value Stream organization.

We recommend a formal meeting at project closure to review the project. The project leader and team present to the people who own the Value Stream and the new cell as well as other management who sponsored the project. This meeting should cover the following items:
- Much of the presentation from the Story Board, or "project diary"
  - Overview of project
  - Objectives
  - Design and implementation
  - Issues and resolution

- Quantitative targets and results
  - Plan vs. Actual
  - Differences, causes, and resolution
- Learnings
  - Implementing continuous flow
  - Support systems
  - Organizational issues
- Recommendations for next steps
  - Other project loops within the Value Stream
  - Projects linking this Value Stream to others
  - Extended Value Stream projects
  - Replication of this cell design in other areas or facilities

DECIDING WHAT'S NEXT

Most Future State Value Stream Maps have several project loops identified. Full benefits of the Lean improvement efforts for the Value Stream cannot be realized by the customer until all loops are implemented. So, don't stop with one loop! Continue until the entire Value Stream is Lean.

Next, look at other product families identified earlier in the Product Family Matrix for similar opportunities.

Then, explore the **Extended Value Stream**, which connects your value stream to those of suppliers and customers. Extended Value Stream Maps include information and material flows as well as product flows. And, they typically include transportation and logistics between facilities.

CONCLUSION

As in any change management effort, a key factor for success is how well the change is managed. For any Lean effort to be successful, people must understand Lean and own the changes made.

Lean is powerful and applies to any Value Stream. Good luck as you unleash this power in your world!

5S, *115*

Accelerated deterioration, *69*

Activity process maps, *28*

Actual output, *66*

Analyze, *6*

Anthropometrics, *130*

Autonomous maintenance, *67*

Available time, *20*

Biomechanics, *130*

Bottleneck, *61*

Buffer stock, *22*

Business value, *2*

Capacity, *20*

Cell, *49*

Combination chart, *101*

Concept layout, *86*

Constant value, *137*

Continuous flow, *37*

Control, *6*

Cycle time, *19*

Debugging, *153*

Defect rate, *20*

Define, *6*

Deployment process maps, *28*

Effective machine cycle, *61*

Elimination techniques, *120*

Ergonomics, *129*

Extended value stream, *159*

External steps, *81*

Final inspection, *136*

Finished goods, *22*

Five-minute shine, *122*

Future State Value Stream Map, *33*

Good output, *66*

Housekeeping checklists, *122*

Ideal sequence, *83*

Implementation, *150*

Implementation plan, *151*

Improve, *6*

In-cycle work, *57*

Internal steps, *81*

Interval, *56*

Inventory turns, *22*

Jidoka, *40*

Kaizen, *46*

Kaizen workshop, *141*

Kanban, *40*

Labor linearity, *103*

Lead time, *19*

Machine cycle, *61*

Measure, *6*

Mistake-proofing, *135*

Mock-up, *151*

Motion economy, *132*

Natural deterioration, *69*

Net operating time, *66*

Number of people, *20*

Operator balance chart, *38*

Organizing concepts, *119*

Out-of-cycle work, *57*

Overall equipment effectiveness, *65*

Overproduction, *34*

Pacemaker, *43*

Pack size, *20*

Pack-out quantity, *20*

Paper kaizen, *59*

Performance measures, *149*

Physical characteristics, *137*

Pilot, *152*

Pitch, *45*

Plan for every part, *88*

Planned cycle time, *95*

Point efficiency, *35*

Poka-Yoke, *135*

Process balance chart, *38*
Process mapping, *27*
Process measures, *149*
Process sequence, *137*
Process steps, *10*
Processing time, *19*
Product family, *9*
Product variation, *20*
Products, *10*
Project "loops", *49*
Pull, *5*
Raw material, *22*
Rework rate, *20*
Red Tag Holding Area, *117*
Running time, *66*
Safety stock, *22*
Scrap rate, *20*
Self inspection, *136*
Set in order, *116*
Setup time, *19*
Shine, *116*
Shipping stock, *22*
Single stack, *59*
SIPOC, *9*
Sort, *116*
Source inspection, *137*
Spaghetti diagram, *12*
Standard work, *107*
Standard work 1, *108*
Standard work 2, *108*
Standard work 3, *108*
Standard work chart, *101*
Standardize, *116*
Strategic value stream map, *9*
Successive inspection, *136*
Supermarket, *36*
Supermarket pull system, *40*

Sustain, *116*
System efficiency, *35*
Takt time, *4*
Time-based value added
   flow analysis, *30*
Toggling, *103*
Total operating time, *66*
Total productive maintenance, *67*
Uptime, *20*
Value added flow analysis, *29*
Value added time, *19*
Value analysis matrix, *30*
Value stream, *1*
Value stream map, *15*
Visual controls, *120*
Visual workplace, *126*
Waste, *2*
Work content, *57*
Work element, *57*
Work-in-process, *22*